HOW SCIENTISTS FIND OUT

A Book about Experimental Medicine
and the Scientific Method

HOW SCIENTISTS
FIND OUT

by William D. Lotspeich

Illustrated by JOHN C. MENIHAN

Little, Brown and Company
BOSTON • TORONTO

Published simultaneously in Canada
by Little, Brown & Company (Canada) Limited

PRINTED IN THE UNITED STATES OF AMERICA

For my children: *Steve, Charlie, and Sylvia*

Contents

HOW SCIENTISTS FIND OUT

I What It's All About

THE IDEA for this book grew out of a series of "doctor stories" I used to tell my children. In each I told about a piece of real research leading to a discovery in medicine, physiology, biology, or chemistry. Some of the stories in this volume, such as the story of vitamin K, come directly from the "doctor stories"; others have been added. The aim of these stories was to tell the children, through real cases, how discovery in research works; how an idea arises and leads to the experiments that test it and mold it, and how the conclusions drawn from the experiments become the thing we call a discovery. Since I am a physician and physiologist, it was natural that the stories should come from medical, biological, and physiological research. However, research in any of the experimental sciences is similar enough so that my stories can tell what research is like in most parts of science.

After a while it became clear that as a group these stories illustrate the whole process of scientific research. Although each story described a complete piece of research, each one illustrated one aspect of the process more than others. For example, the discovery of vitamin

K is a beautiful example of the role of serendipity in research; the two-heart experiment of Dr. Loewi illustrates the place of the carefully planned decisive experiment, and so on. The book, then, presents nine separate stories of research as it was conceived and performed. The theme that ties these stories together is a description of the many-faced process called scientific research.

Young men and women today have read many biographies of scientists, but few have had the opportunity to follow some of these men and women through the actual development of a fine piece of their research. My children were able to understand the stories, and I became convinced that in them lay a rich store of interest for many young people. They speak for themselves with no other trimmings than my attempt to put them into decent English. So, to tell the story of research through these stories is my first objective. Beyond this aim, however, there are other reasons for writing this book.

Today we live in a world fashioned out of the scientific revolution, yet in this world we have two distinct cultures which have difficulty understanding each other. One of these is the scientific, and the other the traditional culture of the humanities: art, philosophy, and letters. It is important that educated people of today know something of both these cultures, for each is a part of the total experience of human existence. So, in a very small way, this book is an attempt to introduce young people to the thinking of experimental science in a way not usually open to them in their science courses. Most of these courses are not experimental, and are presented by teachers who are themselves not acquainted with experimental science from firsthand experience. So they are usually telling about experimental science as outsiders rather than conveying its real meaning from within.

Today, then, we need men and women whose education has forced them to understand the basic ideas in both expressions of man's mind, the arts and the sciences. Often the choice of a career in science is made from the science-fiction idea of what science is, or the career is not chosen at all by young people because they do not really know what it is all about. Therefore it is hoped that this book will both present a truer picture of what experimental science really is, at the same time kindling a deeper interest in it, and stimulate a new desire not to separate it from traditional culture but to incorporate it into the whole experience of life.

II   Stevie Makes a Discovery

THE OTHER EVENING my son Stevie told me they were studying the weather in school, and that he and David wanted to build a weather station to be mounted on top of the barn. They would have a wind-speed indicator, a vane, thermometer, and barometer. During the discussion that followed I asked Steve whether he knew how a barometer works. He had the general idea; told me the weight of the air pressing down on an open pool of mercury forces it up a glass tube sticking down in the mercury. The height of the mercury in the tube then represents the air pressure — expressed in millimeters or inches of mercury. He understood the principle of the instrument perfectly, and we drew a picture of it.

We then went on to discuss a thermometer. He knew that heat means molecules moving faster and this makes the mercury in the thermometer bulb expand up the tube as the temperature rises, and come down again as it falls. I emphasized that a thermometer is different from a barometer; it is all closed, no open part for the air to press on, and in the closed tube above the mercury there is no air, a vacuum. We drew a picture of a thermometer.

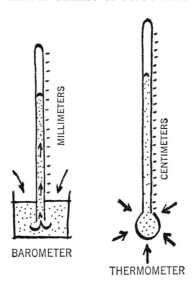

Now I questioned Steve about certain studies he would have to make before he could actually use the thermometer to tell the temperature. "What would you have to do first, Steve, before you could say for sure what temperature is registered at each height of the mercury in the tube?"

"You'd have to put different amounts of heat around the bulb, and measure the height of the mercury with each amount of heat," he replied after a moment's reflection.

"Right," I said. "This must be done with all scientific instruments before we can use them accurately for measurements. This process of determining just how an instrument will behave under known conditions is called 'calibration,' and it's very important if the instrument is to give good results." Stevie nodded understanding.

"Let's see how such a calibration might actually work with a thermometer," I said. "Would you like to?"

"Sure," Steve replied. By now his curiosity was aroused, and he was completely concentrated on the new problem before him.

"Do you know how to make a graph, Stevie?"

"Yes, I think so," he said without hesitation. "You make two lines, one up and the other across and put numbers on them."

"That's right," I said. "You make the lines, and we'll build a graph to calibrate our thermometer." So on a clean piece of paper he drew two lines at right angles to each other.

"Now, Steve," I continued, "we'll have to put some numbers next to these lines to represent the amount of heat and the height of mercury in the tube. So let's put our heat numbers below the cross line and the mercury height ones beside the up and down line. We'll put our numbers an equal distance apart, measuring them with a ruler. We'll speak of the heat as 'degrees' and the height of the mercury as 'centimeters' — each centimeter is a hundredth part of a meter, which is about a yard. When we've put on the numbers we'll make the graph into a square and rule it off into smaller squares so we can find our points on it as we make our measurements with the thermometer."

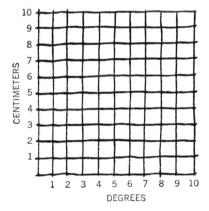

"Now, Stevie," I continued, "suppose I put the thermometer bulb down in water and heat the water one degree. For the moment we don't have to worry about exactly how much heat one degree is; for our purposes let's say it's the change in the hotness of the water caused by putting under it one candle. Now we find that this one candle, which we're calling one degree, makes the mercury rise one centimeter after one minute, and then it rises no higher. Let's show that as a point on the graph where the line from one centimeter crosses the line from one degree. Now let's put two candles under the water. After a minute the mercury stops at two centimeters, and we put that point on the graph. We go on measuring this way and see that for each degree of heat the mercury climbs one centimeter, until by the time we have measured ten degrees we have the mercury up ten centimeters. Now our graph now looks like this with a line connecting the points we have put on it from our calibration experiment."

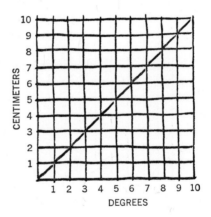

Steve's face lighted up. "Oh, I see," he exclaimed, "once I know this, then I can rule off centimeter numbers on my thermometer tube and put one degree numbers beside each line and then be able to tell the number of degrees each centimeter of mercury means."

"That's just right, Stevie, you see it perfectly," I said

with the excitement a teacher feels when confronted with understanding. "When two things are related like this we say they are 'proportional,' and when the one goes up or down equally with the other, and their graph gives a straight line like ours, we call the relation between the two things a 'direct proportion.' If one of the things we are measuring — and we call these 'variables' — goes down as the other goes up, we say their relation is an 'indirect proportion,' or an 'inverse proportion.' In science we discover and describe relations between things, and try to determine whether the one thing also *causes* the other and *why* it does so."

"Oftentimes," I continued, "we can discover not only whether a *cause* and an *effect* are related, but *how* they are. This can be done by changing the conditions of one or both of the two things and then studying again their relation. When we are studying such relations between variables in an experiment, we must be sure they aren't being changed by something we aren't seeing or hadn't thought about. For this reason we have to control everything in an experiment that can be changed, or cause a change, other than just those things we want to study. I'll tell you a story some other time about controlling experiments; I only mention it here to tell how important a part it plays in an experiment."

Having gone this far with Steve, I decided to go one step further with him in the thermometer study. I said, "Steve, the relations we've seen so far with the thermometer take place when there is a vacuum in the closed tube above the mercury, and we have seen a directly proportional relationship between degrees of heat and rise of the mercury in the tube over a range of ten degrees. I wonder what this relation would be if there were some air in the tube above the mercury?"

Steve thought hard for a while. Finally he said, "Well, if there were air above the mercury, and you heated the thermometer bulb, as the mercury rose in the tube it would push the air together."

"Very true," I replied excitedly. "What would this do to the ability of the mercury to rise in the tube as the temperature rose?"

After a thoughtful pause Steve said, "I guess the pressed air would push back on the mercury so it wouldn't be able to rise so high."

"You're right, absolutely right. You see the whole thing clearly. Now let's go back to your graph and see whether you can draw a line that would show the relationship between temperature and mercury height when there is air in the tube above the mercury."

My pulse was pounding in my temples as I waited to see what he would do. He was in deep concentrated

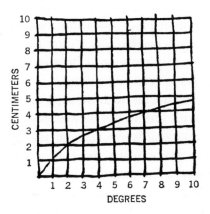

thought, contemplating the graph, moving his pencil along above the straight line. After a few minutes I could see his grip tighten on the pencil; he gave me a questioning sideways glance, and in a half-sure voice said, "I think in that case the line would be a curved one like this. Because the more the mercury rose in the tube, the more it would push the air together and the more the air would push back on the mercury, and this would mean that the mercury could rise less and less. Is that right?"

"It sure is!" I shouted with joy. "It sure is! That's just exactly right. You've seen something tonight that's completely new for you for the first time in your life. You've not only been able to see how two things are related, but how a change in one changes the relation; and you've been able to see it in your imagination. This is a very important thing for a research scientist to be able to do, and not all of them can. It's one of the things that separates the really good ones from the rest. You've learned a whole lot about how to use your mind, to think clearly, to see for yourself a relation between things under different conditions. You now know a lot about what the scientific method is."

III Are There Good Controls?

A<small>T THE</small> very base of the brain in the middle of the head there is a small area that plays a big part in the regulation of appetite and growth. This area lies just above the roof of the mouth and consists of two main parts that are connected. The upper part is called the *hypothalamus*, and it forms the bottom of the brain at this point. Extending down from this hypothalamus is a stalk, or stem, a few millimeters long. At the end of this stalk is a little gland about the size and shape of a small grape; it is called the *pituitary gland*. The stem connecting it to the hypothalamus above is the *pituitary stalk*. The pituitary is not, strictly speaking, a part of the brain proper, but it is connected with it and works very closely with it in several ways. The pituitary gland lies in a small bony cavity in the base of the skull; the cavity is called the *sella turcica* because it reminded some early anatomist of a "Turkish saddle" — *sella turcica* in Latin.

I will tell first about some pituitary gland research in which food intake had to be controlled in one way; then return later to another piece of research on the way the hypothalamus regulates appetite. In both pieces of research food intake became an important part of the experimental design, but in a quite different way in each one.

The pituitary gland is a very important organ because it secretes into the bloodstream a number of different chemicals, called *hormones*. These regulate the rate at which some other glands, such as the thyroid, adrenals, and sex glands, secrete their hormones. The pituitary also secretes another hormone that plays an important part in regulating body growth, and this is the one that will interest us here. Some kinds of dwarfs do not have enough of this pituitary *growth hormone*, and giants had too much of it during their youth when they were still growing. They just didn't stop growing when they should have.

A new kind of research on this growth hormone of the pituitary gland was made possible in 1925 when Dr. P. E. Smith at Columbia University perfected a simple way to remove the pituitary gland in laboratory white rats. He was able to make a small hole, with a dental drill, into the *sella turcica* from below through the roof of the mouth, and very easily suck out the pituitary gland tissue with a medicine dropper. He noted that these animals failed to grow properly after removal of the gland in this way.

Four years earlier, H. M. Evans and J. A. Long, at the University of California, produced giant rats by injecting them with crude extracts of pituitary glands. It was shown later that after pituitary removal, injection with such extracts not only maintained the normal rate of growth, but in larger amounts it actually caused giant rats.

How can we tell that the increased weight in such treated animals represents true growth? Weight gain can result from an increase in water or fat in the body; but in true growth, cells divide and the total amount of tissue protein in the body increases in proportion to water and salts in the body. Measurements of the body constituents in these pituitary-treated rats showed that they had truly grown in this way; in fact, as they increased body protein their body fat decreased, as if the energy for making the new tissue had come from the combustion of body fat.

Later, Drs. H. M. Evans and C. H. Li, still working at the University of California, succeeded in isolating from beef pituitary glands a highly purified growth hormone. This protein substance injected in very small amounts causes a dramatic increase in growth of adult rats that have already stopped growing. One milligram a day (one thousandth of a gram) will cause an adult female rat to gain ten grams in ten days, and in a rat without the pituitary the amount required to cause this same rate of weight gain is much less; a few thousandths of a milligram per day. This gives some idea of how powerful this growth-stimulating substance is.

Now, of course, it takes food to grow. So here the investigator naturally asks experimental questions about the relation of food intake to this growth-stimulating effect of the pituitary hormone. One of the first questions he asks is this: Does the hormone simply stimulate the animal's appetite, and make him grow more because he eats more? Or does it cause his body to use the same amount of food more efficiently? To answer these questions experimentally, the intake of food must be carefully *controlled*. How is this done?

There are two ways to do it. One is called "limit-feeding," and the other "pair-feeding." In limit-feeding, the experimenter first determines how much food an untreated rat will eat completely in one day and still maintain normal body weight. He then allows just this amount of food to all rats, treated and untreated, and checks each day to see that each animal has eaten all its food. In the method of pair-feeding, the experimenter measures the amount of food eaten by the untreated (control) group of animals on day one. Then on day two he restricts each treated animal to the amount eaten by its control the day before. Thus, the treated animal lags behind its pair-fed control by one day, but over a longer period both groups consume the same amount of food.

In experiments with pituitary extracts — or purified growth hormone — food intake has been controlled in both these ways, and no matter which method is used the answer is the same; new growth occurs after treatment with the hormone even though food intake stays the same. This is a beautifully controlled experiment and tells us a startling thing, namely, that the pituitary growth hormone doesn't stimulate growth by making the animal eat more food, but it makes the body use its food more efficiently for growth. What exactly do we mean by this?

An engine's "efficiency" is described in terms of the

proportion of its fuel energy it uses for work, and the proportion it loses as heat. This energy lost as heat does not do any useful work in the machine. Suppose a gallon of fuel contains one thousand calories of energy, that is *potential energy;* the machine will have a fifty-per-cent efficiency if from the combustion of one gallon of fuel 500 calories appear as work, and 500 as heat.

In the body the process of building new tissue is a type of *biologic work;* energy from food is required. If we can use more food calories for this work, and lose less of them as heat then our body "machine" is working with greater efficiency. This is what growth hormone makes the body do.

When growth hormone is injected into the rat, the experimenter observes a number of interesting changes in the animal and these are associated with this greater efficiency in use of food for growth. One of the earliest changes is a decrease in the loss of nitrogen in the urine. Nitrogen is a part of each amino acid, and therefore of the proteins. As new proteins are built more nitrogen is stored in the body, so less appears in the urine. Fat is carried from the fat parts of the body to the liver where it is burned as a very efficient fuel source to provide energy for growth. This mobilization of fat is recognized because the amount of fat acids in the blood rises, and the amount of fat stored in the body goes down. Sugar is another energy fuel, and after growth hormone injection the amount of sugar in the blood at first rises; then later the blood sugar goes down as the sugar is used by the tissues. Amino acids in the blood decrease as they are drawn into the tissues for manufacture into protein.

These experiments with controlled food intake were needed to discover these important facts about the pituitary hormone that regulates growth.

Now let's look at another important mechanism that is regulated up above the pituitary in the hypothalamus. This one has to do with the regulation of food intake rather than the efficiency of its use in the body.

Our intake of food is directed by two quite different things: hunger and appetite. *Hunger* refers to a painful sensation in the area of the stomach. It comes on three hours or so after eating, feels like cramps, occurs in waves that last a few minutes, then pass away only to return again after a while. The sensation of hunger is relieved by eating. *Appetite* is something quite different. It is a much more complicated feeling, described as a general desire for food. It is an emotional thing brought on by smelling or seeing food, or just thinking about it. Appetite can be present without hunger or the opposite can also be true, there may be no appetite in people who need food and experience the pain of hunger. Even people without stomachs can sometimes feel appetite.

Hunger is directly caused by hard contractions of the stomach, but the sensation of appetite arises in the brain from a much more complicated relation between functions of the brain and the digestive tract. One of the most important brain "centers" of appetite is in the hypothalamus. How do we know, and how does this center work?

The first direct answers to these questions came from experiments performed at the Medical School of Northwestern University in 1940 by two physiologists, Drs.

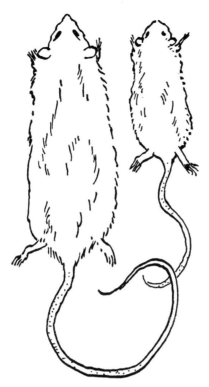

Hetherington and Ranson. They used an ingenious instrument that can be fitted to the head of an animal under anesthesia. It is called a *stereotaxic instrument*, and by making use of carefully worked out geometric planes and angles, it allows the experimenter to insert fine wire needle electrodes with great accuracy into very small regions of the brain. Hetherington and Ranson placed their electrodes in the hypothalami of rats, and with an electric heating current running through them they were able to destroy very small parts of the hypothalamus. Later under the microscope they could check exactly where this destroyed area — or lesion — had been. They noticed a remarkable change in these rats with hypothalamic lesions: they became very large, and the cause was fat; they simply became very, very fat. Why?

Hetherington and Ranson made quite large lesions, and noticed that their rats became rather inactive after the operation. They explained the fatness that gradually developed as the result of this reduction in physical activity. The rat spent less food energy in bodily activity; so he turned it into fat instead.

Three years later, in 1943, these same experiments were repeated and refined at Yale University by Drs. Brobeck, Tepperman, and Long. These investigators were able to make fat rats, just like those of Hetherington and Ranson; only their lesions in the hypothalamus were not nearly so big, and the animals did not show such loss of activity. They noticed what Hetherington and Ranson had not seen — that their rats showed a tremendous increase in food intake after the operation; in fact some started gobbling food even before they were fully recovered from the anesthesia.

Brobeck and his associates discovered that this increased appetite occurred when their lesion — a quite small one — was in the lower middle part of the hypothalamus. Their rats ate as much food as they were given, far beyond their body's needs, and reached body weights of five and six hundred grams, compared to one or two hundred grams for their normal controls. Now came an important observation. When the food intake of these lesion rats was limited to that of the controls they maintained perfectly normal body weight. So there was no change in the way these hypothalamic-lesion rats used their food energy — as there was in those treated with growth hormone — they just had huge appetites and ate themselves fat, the way any person does who eats more than he needs.

These fascinating experiments, with food intake controlled, showed that there is an area in the lower middle part of the hypothalamus that has something to do with appetite control. Does this mean that there is another brain region somewhere that stimulates appetite, and that is normally held in check by this middle area? If so, then to destroy the middle area would release this other "appetite center" which would then produce an unchecked stimulation of the appetite.

Further research has supported this idea. An Indian physiologist, Dr. Anand, working with Dr. Brobeck, made lesions further out in the side part of the hypothalamus, and found that these animals stopped eating altogether. They could be kept alive with feeding by stomach tube, but refused to eat by themselves. Their appetite was completely gone, and they starved to death unless fed by stomach tube. Dr. Anand went on to show that electrical stimulation of the middle hypothalamic center causes the animal to eat less, and stimulation of the side part causes him to eat more.

So a clearer picture of the origin of appetite began to emerge. These two "centers" in the brain's hypothalamus act with each other to create a balance between *appetite* (the desire for food) and *satiety* (the feeling that you've eaten enough). When one or the other of these two gets out of balance for some reason, the appetite goes up or down and we have people who become too fat or too thin.

Dr. Jean Mayer of Harvard University thinks these feeding "centers" are sensitive to the sugar level in the blood. Certainly some blood substance must stimulate or repress them, and the blood sugar idea seems as good as any at present. Just as the thermostat in our houses causes the furnace to turn off or on automatically as room temperature rises or falls, so Mayer believes these appetite centers act like a "glucostat," stimulating or inhibiting the appetite — and thus food intake — as the blood glucose rises or falls from some ideal level set by nature in the body.

Dr. Alfred Froehlich had a boy in his office in Vienna about sixty-three years ago who was becoming too fat. The fat was being laid down in his hips and breast so that he looked more like a woman as time went on. Dr. Froehlich found the boy had a tumor of the pituitary gland at the base of his brain and also noticed that he had a very big appetite. Froehlich concluded that the boy's fatness was caused by the tumor of the pituitary gland. We now know from the research I discussed above that it was overeating caused by destruction of that part of the hypothalamus that signals when one has eaten enough. The female distribution of the fat was probably caused by abnormal amounts of female hormones secreted by cells in the pituitary tumor. The pituitary gland, as it grew larger, couldn't expand downward because of the bony *sella turcica;* so it had to grow up. As it did so it produced pressure on the hypothalamus right above it, and the increased appetite with fatness was the first change noticed. Nature, through disease, had produced a lesion in the hypothalamus like those made by the researchers with electrodes. Without the controlled experiments of Hetherington, Ranson, Brobeck, Tepperman, and Long, the true nature of this situation would not have been understood.

Dr. Bernardo Houssay in Argentina discovered that if he removed the pituitary gland in a dog with diabetes, the diabetes almost disappeared. We know that removal of the pituitary in a normal animal causes loss of appetite. Maybe Houssay's experiment improved the diabetes simply because the animal stopped eating. What a trap Houssay would have fallen into if he had not thought of this possibility and controlled it! But he did, and even when given their normal amount of food his diabetic dogs were improved by pituitary gland removal. Drs. Long and Lukens showed that removal of the adrenal glands also improves diabetes in the experimental animals. They too thought of food intake because animals without adrenals practically stop eating.

So controls are things the experimenter has to think about when he originally designs the experiment, and then again when he interprets his results. He must ask himself, "Is my explanation of the results the real one, or am I only seeing a side effect that has nothing to do with my explanation?" To see these possibilities in research requires the finest kind of imagination and its intelligent use.

IV Serendipity

A PIECE of research starts when the investigator asks a specific question. The experiments that follow are designed to answer this question. Occasionally, however, the research scientist discovers something along the way that is quite different from what he had in mind, and sometimes these chance discoveries are of equal or greater importance than what he was originally looking for. The scientist must always be alert enough to recognize these unexpected events and see their true importance rather than explain them as "errors" in experimental technique or design.

These happy unexpected discoveries are examples of what has been called serendipity. This word has an interesting history. It comes from the arabic word *Sarandib* meaning Ceylon. *Sarandib* comes from two ancient Sanskrit words: *Simhala* meaning Singhalese, the langauge of Ceylon, and *Dvipa* meaning island. So the word refers to the island of Ceylon. The word serendipity was coined by the British novelist Horace Walpole when he referred to a tale, *The Three Princes of Serendip*. In their travels these princes were always making chance or wise discoveries they had not originally sought. From this beginning Walpole's word has come into common usage.

There have been many examples of serendipity in research, but one of the finest was the discovery of vitamin K by the Danish biochemist Henrik Dam. The story began in Copenhagen around the year 1928. Dr. Dam was interested in a fat-like substance called *cholesterol* which is present in butter, eggs, and certain other fatty foods. It circulates in the blood and is of particular interest today because of its possible relation to the process of hardening of the arteries. Dr. Dam wanted to know whether animals could make their own cholesterol from other chemicals in the body, even though there was no cholesterol in their diet.

For his experiments he used chicks kept on a ration free of all cholesterol. His plan was to measure their blood concentration of cholesterol and compare it to that of chicks kept on a similar diet with cholesterol added. The diets he used were completely artificial, that is, they were made up from milk protein, sugar, vegetable oil, minerals, and the known vitamins.

During his experiments Dr. Dam began noticing, quite by chance, a curious thing; his chicks reared on the cholesterol-free diet developed hemorrhages under the skin, in muscles, and other organs. This happened even though all known vitamins and other food stuffs had been added to the artificial diet.

It was quickly found that the blood of these chicks took longer to clot than normal. It was known that a tendency to bleed easily is a part of the disease called *scurvy*, caused by a lack of vitamin C in the diet. There-

fore Dr. Dam tried pure vitamin C on his chicks, but it failed to prevent the bleeding. He also knew that it couldn't be the absence of cholesterol in the diet because his experiments had already shown beyond doubt that the chicks could make their own cholesterol in their bodies. So the question he originally posed had been positively answered.

He next tried the oil of wheat germ and cod-liver oil, both rich sources of vitamins A, D, and E, which had been removed when the diet was freed of cholesterol by fat extraction procedures. These oils also failed to protect against the bleeding disease. Finally Dr. Dam and his associates found that the only way they could prevent the bleeding was by adding whole cereals and the leaves of certain green vegetables to the artificial diet. This meant that in one of these he had added some food factor which protected his chicks. Since this substance was none of the vitamins then known to man, Dr. Dam felt quite sure that he had discovered by chance a new vitamin. He knew only that it had these characteristics: it was extracted from food along with fats; it was not present in cod-liver oil or wheat-germ oil, and it had some vital role in the clotting of blood.

This was in 1934, some six years after the research had started. Dam soon found that the vitamin was present not only in whole cereals and green leafy vegetables but also in tomatoes and certain meats, particularly pig liver. In 1935 Dr. Dam named the new clotting factor *vitamin K*. The letter K had not yet been used for a vitamin, and he used it because K is the first letter of the

word "koagulation," the way our word "coagulation" is
spelled in the Danish language.

The research now centered on two large problems:
first, the isolation of the pure vitamin and the determi-
nation of its exact chemical nature, and second an understanding of how it works in the normal process of
blood coagulation. The first problem was brilliantly
solved partly in Dr. Dam's own laboratory when he and
his associates obtained the pure vitamin as a yellow oil
extracted from dried alfalfa leaves. Shortly thereafter
two biochemists, Drs. Doisey and Fieser, working in
separate laboratories in the United States, determined
the exact structure of the vitamin molecule. It turned
out to belong to a class of chemicals known as the
naphthoquinones. Artificial naphthoquinones are now
produced which have even greater blood-clotting activity than the naturally occurring vitamin K.

The problem of how vitamin K works has also been
partially solved. In blood there is a dissolved protein
called *fibrinogen*. When blood coagulates the small fibrinogen molecules join together into long chains which
come out of their dissolved form as long needle-shaped
crystals called *fibrin*, and it is these that mat together to
make the jelly-like clot. In order for the dissolved *fibrinogen* molecules to join together into the undissolved
fibrin, an important blood substance called *prothrombin* is needed. This is made in the liver and released
from there into the blood. Dr. Dam found that the vitamin K-deficient chicks had very little prothrombin in
their blood and therefore it did not clot. He also found
that if he added vitamin K to the diet the blood pro-

thrombin increased and the blood then clotted normally. Several studies have shown that the liver is necessary for this vitamin K effect. If the vitamin is added directly to blood from deficient chicks, the prothrombin in it does not increase. Furthermore, some doctors in New York showed that vitamin K given to dogs without livers does not change the blood prothrombin content, but does when the liver is present. Therefore vitamin K, which gets into the body with the food, is absorbed from the small intestine, goes by the bloodstream to the liver, and there somehow helps the liver to make the important blood-clotting substance, prothrombin.

This chance discovery of vitamin K by Dr. Dam, this bit of serendipity, and the understanding of how vitamin K affects blood clotting through its role in prothrombin production, have had a significant effect on physiology and medicine. Let us look at a few examples.

Sometimes people develop a brownish-green color of the skin and the whites of the eyes; this condition is called *jaundice*. It results from the deposit in the tissues of breakdown products of hemoglobin, the oxygen-carrying pigment of red blood cells. These products are normally excreted through the liver into the intestine with the bile. If too many red blood cells are destroyed, or if the free passage of bile from liver to intestine is obstructed, these greenish-brown pigments are deposited in the body's tissues, and jaundice results.

Surgeons have known for a long time that certain patients with jaundice are very poor surgical risks because they bleed uncontrollably when their tissues are cut with a scalpel at operation, and many such persons have died in the past. Now, however, as a result of the vitamin K discovery, this need not happen.

Vitamin K is an oily substance, and like other fats or oils it requires the presence of bile for its absorption from the intestine. If the bile passages from liver to intestine are blocked, no bile reaches the intestine and the vitamin K taken with the food — or made by the bacteria in the intestine — cannot be absorbed from the intestine and carried to the liver. For this reason, the liver production of vitamin K falls off, and the blood clots poorly. Today when patients with bile obstruction and jaundice are seen by the doctor he will not operate to remove the obstruction until he has measured the amount of prothrombin in the blood, and brought the clotting time to normal with vitamin K injections. After this he can operate knowing that his patient will not bleed to death when he makes his healing incision.

Sometimes a few days after birth babies may bleed easily, and they have been found to have too little prothrombin in their blood. Vitamin K restores their prothrombin to normal. Curiously, though, nothing is wrong with their bile flow or liver; it is the lack of bacteria in their intestines that is to blame. Scientists have found that the normal, beneficial bacteria in the intestine make vitamin K for us, and thus supply at least part of our needs — even when vitamin K intake in the food is low. For a few days after birth babies have no bacteria in their intestines. Therefore their only supply of vitamin K is what they receive from their mother before birth, or with their mother's milk after birth. If the vitamin K supply from these sources is not enough before the baby grows a good crop of his own intestinal bacteria, a bleeding tendency may develop, a condition called *hemorrhagic disease of the newborn*. Now, however, with our knowledge of vitamin K, we can give mothers an extra supply of the vitamin before birth of the baby, and the hemorrhagic disease — once a danger and a puzzle — is easily prevented.

Sometimes when sulfa drugs or penicillin-like medicines are given by mouth for long periods — particularly to babies or persons who aren't eating much — these necessary and helpful intestinal bacteria are killed. If adequate amounts of vitamin K are not given, a deficiency of this vitamin may result because there are not enough bacteria making it. When doctors first saw this happening in otherwise normal people they were puzzled until someone saw its relation to the vitamin K story. Now this complication of an otherwise beneficial treatment can be prevented; or if it occurs, quickly recognized and corrected with vitamin K injections.

There is still another story of discovery that is related to the vitamin K chapter. A brilliant series of experiments by Dr. Karl Link at the University of Wisconsin joined his originally unrelated findings to those of Dr. Dam. Dr. Link was interested in the cause and treatment of a bleeding disease in cattle. This condition was a complete mystery and each year took a terrible toll of cattle life on the farms of Wisconsin near where Link worked.

Dr. Link soon noticed a relation between the eating of spoiled sweet-clover hay and the bleeding disease. He immediately prepared extracts of the spoiled sweet

Dr. Link at Wisconsin

clover, injected them into healthy cows, and produced the bleeding disease. He also found the cow's blood prothrombin reduced — just as in vitamin K deficiency. Could it be, he thought, that the clover — normally a rich source of vitamin K — contains a substance, when it is spoiled, that actually produces a vitamin K deficiency?

This question led Dr. Link to purify his spoiled sweetclover extract, and finally to isolate from it a pure substance which proved to be the powerful bleeding agent in cattle and certain other animals, and man as well. He called the new chemical *dicoumarol* and announced that the cause of hemorrhagic disease in cattle had been discovered.

But the story was not to end there, for soon this substance, so poisonous to cattle, was turned to the benefit of man. Link showed that dicoumarol blocks the ability of vitamin K to stimulate prothrombin formation in the liver. He also found that a lot of vitamin K can block the anti-vitamin K action of dicoumarol.

This was very fortunate, because often the doctor wishes to reduce — on purpose — the clotting capacity of the blood in people who are forming clots inside their veins. Up to the time of dicoumarol the only drug available for this purpose was *heparin*, which doctors don't like to use because they cannot easily control the bad bleeding that sometimes occurs if too much is given. Now, however, with dicoumarol we can simply give vitamin K if bleeding develops and the doctor feels safer in a touchy situation.

After their heart attacks, President Eisenhower and

President (then Senator) Johnson were given a dicoumarol drug to reduce the chance of forming any more
clots in the heart, brain, or lungs. So with dicoumarol
on the one hand and vitamin K on the other, the patient
being treated for clots in his veins lives in a neat balance
between life and death, where the pendulum swings between the dicoumarol in one syringe and vitamin K in
another.

The development of dicoumarol in Link's laboratory
was followed by his recognition that its deadly qualities
could be of another use to mankind. A slight modifica-
tion of the dicoumarol molecule produced a chemical
that proved very poisonous to rats and mice when eaten
in small amounts. It blocked their vitamin K, and made
them bleed inside. With his characteristic sense of hu-
mor this more powerful dicoumarol was named by Link
warfarin, and it is now marketed everywhere as our
most successful rat poison. The name warfarin was
coined by Link from the words "Wisconsin Alumni Research Foundation Incorporated," the source of the
funds that supported his research at the University of
Wisconsin.

So from chance observation of skin hemorrhages in
chicks by an alert scientist in Denmark, and ingenious
research with spoiled sweet clover in Wisconsin, grew
this remarkable story of discovery. Vitamin K and dicoumarol have given us powerful tools in our work to
preserve health and combat disease. The role of serendipity in research must not be overlooked.

V   Sometimes It Happens Quickly

Nerve cells have a main body and passing out from it a long thread-like tail called the *axone*. Sometimes these axones are very long, traveling from the cell body in the spinal cord all the way down the leg to a muscle in the sole of the foot. Nerves are really bundles of these axones on their way to muscles, glands, or other nerve cells.

Physiologists have long wondered how nerve impulses cause the effects they produce in their target organs. If you look at the endings of nerves under a very high-powered microscope, you can see that there is a very small space between the ends of the axone and the surface of the cells in the organ. How does the nerve impulse cross this tiny gap to the organ? Is it electricity that jumps across the gap? Or is it possible that the nerve impulse somehow causes the secretion of some chemical at the nerve ending, and then this substance affects the cells of the organ to produce the changes we see in it when the nerve is stimulated?

About the time of the American Civil War, a famous French physiologist, Dr. Claude Bernard, did an experiment that suggested to him this second idea. He used frogs. High around one leg he placed a tourniquet so nothing could reach that leg through the blood circulation. Then he injected under the skin of the lower back a powerful poison called *curare*. Primitive tribes in South America and Africa had for many years dipped their hunting arrows in solutions of curare. When struck by such an arrow the hunted animal is quickly paralyzed and dies. Dr. Bernard now observed some most important things in his curare-injected frogs. If he stimulated the nerve to the leg with blood circulation blocked, the muscles of that leg twitched strongly, showing that nerve, muscles, and the junctions between them were all functioning normally. By contrast, however, when he stimulated the main nerve to the other leg — the one whose blood circulation had not been stopped — there was absolutely no contraction of the muscles; the leg was paralyzed.

If Claude Bernard had stopped right there, he never would have seen the true meaning of the experiment; he simply would have concluded that curare paralyzes the muscles when allowed to reach them through the bloodstream. But he went one important step further; he stimulated these "paralyzed" muscles directly — not through their nerves, but by placing his stimulating electrodes directly on the exposed muscle surface. To his surprise and delight he saw that this caused the muscles to contract just as vigorously as those of the other leg when they were stimulated through their nerve.

So after injecting curare there wasn't anything wrong with the muscle itself, but rather the impulse going

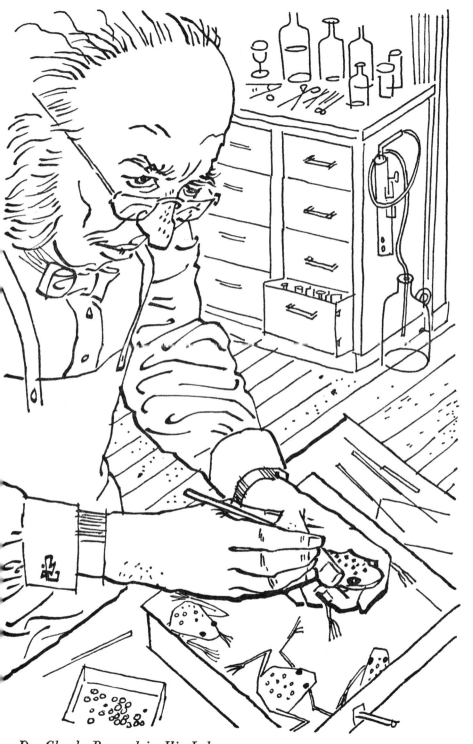

Dr. Claude Bernard in His Laboratory

down the nerve was somehow blocked and couldn't get across the nerve ending to the muscle. Did the curare perhaps block the secretion of some chemical at the nerve ending, a chemical that then causes the muscle to contract?

For such a mechanism to work well this chemical transmitter substance would have to exist at the nerve ending for only an instant; otherwise the effects of the nerve's activity would be prolonged and clumsy, rather than delicate and very short as they are. To achieve this sort of action physiologists reasoned that there must be some enzyme at the nerve ending itself that quickly destroys the transmitter chemical as soon as its action has taken place. We shall see later that this is so.

This idea — that nerves secrete chemicals at their endings and that these chemicals bring about the nerve effects — was proved beyond doubt by a remarkably simple experiment performed by Dr. Otto Loewi in Graz, Austria, at Easter time in 1920. He was then Professor of Pharmacology at the University of Graz. On earlier visits to England he had come to know some of the men at Cambridge and the University of London who were studying that part of the nervous system — the *autonomic branch* — that controls our involuntary functions, such as heartbeat, stomach and intestinal movements, gland secretion, and contraction of the urinary bladder. In discussions with these men, Dr. Loewi had begun to think deeply about how nerves exert their effects on organs.

As far back as 1903, following discussions with Dr. Fletcher at Cambridge, Loewi had the idea that chemical transmitters exist at nerve endings. The idea seemed particularly attractive to him because stimulation of some nerves causes the organ to be excited — for instance, the heart to speed up — while stimulating other nerves inhibits the organ's activity. For example, stimulation of the vagus nerve to the heart causes the heart to slow down or even stop altogether. Dr. Loewi had also been struck by the fact that certain drugs mimic both these excitatory and inhibitory effects of nerve stimulation. So the chemical transmitter idea seemed to him attractive, but he couldn't think of a way to test it by experiment.

Dr. Loewi

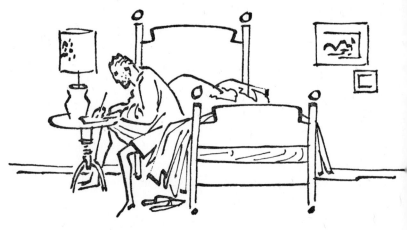

From 1903 to 1920 this interest lay in the back of his mind while he worked actively on other things. Then during the night before Easter, 1920, he awoke and put a few notes down on a piece of paper and fell asleep again. Next morning at six o'clock he remembered that he had written down something important during the night, but when he looked at the slip of paper he was unable to make out his half-asleep scrawl. The next night at 3 A.M. the idea returned, and he woke up with it sharply focused in his mind; it was a perfectly clear design for an experiment to test the chemical transmission idea. Not trusting his memory — or the legibility of his night handwriting — Dr. Loewi got up immediately and went to the laboratory where he performed the now famous experiment that proved the correctness of the chemical transmitter idea he had suggested seventeen years earlier! This is how he did it.

The heart of the frog will continue to beat for many hours outside the body if it is carefully handled and bathed with a solution closely resembling the frog's own body fluids. Taking advantage of this fact, Dr. Loewi removed the hearts from two frogs, leaving the nerves to one heart, and removing all the nerves to the other one. Both hearts were now attached to glass tubes, so they could be irrigated with the body fluid solution and at the same time have their rate of beating recorded on a moving piece of graph paper.

Now, the vagus nerves to the first heart were stimulated electrically, and in characteristic fashion this caused the heart to stop. The stimulation was continued for a few minutes. Then some of the fluid that had bathed this heart during the vagus stimulation was transferred to the second heart — the one that had no nerves. To Dr. Loewi's delight this second heart slowed down just as if its vagus nerves had been stimulated, but since it had no nerves the slowing had to be caused by some chemical released in the first heart when its vagus nerves were stimulated. Next, he caused the first heart to speed up by electrical stimulation of its accelerator nerves, and in like fashion the second heart accelerated when bathed with fluid from the first heart.

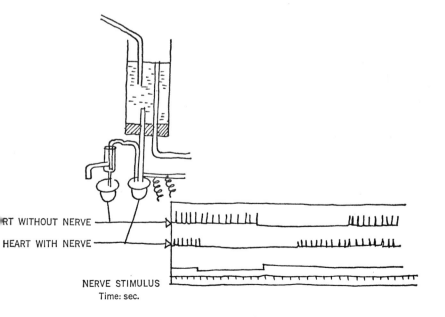

RT WITHOUT NERVE

HEART WITH NERVE

NERVE STIMULUS
Time: sec.

This beautifully simple experiment proved that some substances are released in an organ — presumably at or near its nerve endings — when certain nerves are stimulated, and that these substances act on the organ to produce the nerve effect. The experiment also showed that there is more than one such substance. In Dr. Loewi's case the accelerator nerves released a heart-speeding chemical, and the vagus nerves a heart-slowing one.

A series of elegant laboratory studies since Dr. Loewi's have identified these substances chemically and told us a great deal about how they work. Sir Henry Dale, a great British physiologist — and dear friend of Dr. Loewi's — proved that Loewi's vagus substance is a chemical called *acetylcholine*. Moreover it has been shown that acetylcholine is released at many other nerve endings in the body, and has effects on many different body functions such as digestive-juice secretion, urination, and body muscle action. It was therefore most fitting that Loewi and Dale should both be awarded the Nobel Prize for Medicine in 1936 for their pioneer work in the discovery of these important chemical transmitters of nerve impulses.

The accelerator substance was later shown to be a chemical closely related to *adrenalin*, the hormone secreted by the middle part of the adrenal gland. Dr. Elliot in England had already seen the similarity between the effects of injecting adrenalin and stimulating the group of nerves to which the heart accelerators belong, the *sympathetic* nerves. In recent years the Swedish biochemist von Euler has shown that the substance liberated at the sympathetic nerve endings is not adrenalin itself, but a very closely related substance called *noradrenalin.*

The discovery of these chemical transmitters has opened up a whole new area of disease treatment with drugs. I mentioned earlier that for these chemical transmitters to work quickly there must be *enzymes* located near the nerve endings which cause the rapid destruction of the transmitter chemical. These destroying enzymes have been discovered and they act just as predicted.

Sometimes it is desirable for doctors to prolong the action of a nerve impulse transmitter, and one way to do this is to use a drug that will block the action of the destroying enzyme. Such a drug is *belladonna*, commonly used in eye drops to dilate the pupil so the doctor can see more easily inside the eye. The substance acetylcholine — the heart-slowing chemical released at vagusnerve endings — is also released in the circular muscle controlling the eye's pupil when impulses reach it over one of the eye nerves. This acetylcholine causes the pupil to dilate. Belladonna prevents the acetylcholine normally secreted in the eye from being destroyed, so the pupil stays dilated as long as the belladonna stays in the eye.

Today it is often necessary for surgeons to stop all breathing movements during an operation, for instance when removing all or a part of a lung. Pharmacologists — those who study the way drugs affect body function — have recently devised a substance, called *succinylcholine*, that paralyzes all the body's muscles including those used for breathing. This substance is closely related to acetylcholine, and it was made artificially with the normal action of acetylcholine in mind.

Acetylcholine is secreted at the endings of all nerves going to the muscles that make the body move; these are the muscles of the skeleton. The diaphragm and muscles between the ribs which control respiration are also skeletal muscles, just like the biceps or the calf muscles of the leg. Succinylcholine, when injected into the bloodstream, gets into the nerve endings in these skeletal muscles and changes them temporarily, so they can't react to acetylcholine. As a result the muscles are paralyzed, and this is exactly what the surgeon wants during the operation.

The beauty of succinylcholine comes from the fact that it can be rapidly destroyed by the same enzymes that break down acetylcholine. So when the surgeon wants its effect stopped, he simply stops giving it; what is left in the muscles is destroyed, and they regain their power to react to acetylcholine, the natural stimulus to contraction released from the nerves ending in the muscle cells.

These considerations about the significance of a discovery and the consequences that follow a new research method, we shall find also in the case of chromatography, discussed later. We always build on what has gone before, but seldom has so much to build upon opened up as quickly as it did with Dr. Otto Loewi's simple and decisive experiment with the two frog hearts that early Easter morning back in 1920.

VI   Sometimes It Happens Slowly

CHARLES DARWIN lived in England from 1809 to 1882. Before him, man's beliefs about the history of the earth and living things were quite different than they are today. Darwin published his theory of evolution in his famous book, *The Origin of Species*, in 1859. This book described his theory that man, animals, and plants have gradually evolved from common ancestors into their present form over millions of years. He believed that the cause of this evolution was a process he called natural selection in which only those species that were fitted to live in their surroundings survived; others became extinct.

Darwin's book burst upon the mid-nineteenth-century world like a bombshell and set the fires of controversy raging between churchmen and scientists. The reasons for this will be clear as we go along, but our main questions now are these: Where did Darwin get his ideas? How did he develop them? Why did he take so long to bring them to their final form?

With the exception of a few daring and original thinkers, it was generally believed, before Darwin, that the world and all its living creatures had been made in one week, as told in the Old Testament story of Genesis. It was believed that the earth and its life had then progressed through a series of great catastrophes, like the flood that Noah and all his animals survived in the Ark. In each of these catastrophes the earth's surface was torn apart, new mountains and seas were formed, and in the great flood that followed all life was created again by the almighty hand of God.

Darwin's own grandfather, Erasmus Darwin, was one of the first of a group of daring thinkers who challenged this view. He believed that man and animals were descended from common ancestors and that during the process the characteristics of all living organisms had been gradually changed as a result of use and disuse. These changes were then transmitted to the young of each succeeding generation.

This view was like the one published by the great French biologist Lamarck at about this same time, known as his "theory of the transmission of acquired characteristics." For example, the giraffe was believed by Lamarck to have *evolved* over millions of years from a small prehistoric deer-like animal which found food on the ground more and more scarce. In search of a new source of food he looked upward into trees and began eating the lower leaves. In reaching ever higher for his food supply his neck was gradually stretched, and it became longer and longer until he was slowly transformed into a giraffe. This "acquired characteristic" — the long neck — was transmitted to succeeding generations, and thus a giraffe *evolved* from some earlier quite different form.

There were a number of other men whose ideas influenced Charles Darwin and led him to his own theory of evolution. One of these was the French naturalist Buffon (1707-1788), who became interested in the study of early marine animal fossils he found on mountaintops far from their original ocean. He correctly concluded that these mountains used to be beneath the sea in which these same animals once swam, and he was the first to create a modern picture of the evolution of living things. His ideas had also impressed Erasmus Darwin.

Another French naturalist was Cuvier, whose life (1769-1832) overlapped the latter part of Buffon's. Like Buffon, he saw in the rocks and their embedded fossils a whole succession of animal populations representing now extinct species of the past.

The Scottish physician James Hutton (1726-1797), walking the Highlands of Scotland, saw — as Buffon had — that these fossils occurred in layers, and this suggested to him their slow, orderly deposit over a long period of time rather than in a series of great catastrophes. In the small Highland brooks carrying their deposits of earth from mountaintop to valley, Hutton also saw the evolutionary process of erosion and renewal of the earth, and realized how gradual a process it is.

William Smith (1769-1839), a British civil engineer, was a builder of canals, and in their clean-cut rock walls he saw these same layers of fossils. He noticed that fossils similar to one another appeared in different layers. This led him to believe that the changes he saw in these animals, preserved from different ages of the distant past, couldn't have happened suddenly, but had to be gradual. He also noticed that the further back we go the less like present-day animals and plants these fossils become.

Perhaps the one who affected Charles Darwin most was the British geologist Charles Lyell, who lived from 1797 to 1875. It was he who finally discarded the "catastrophic" idea once and for all. He became Darwin's teacher and colleague. He saw that ancient times were just like his; that rocks are still being laid down by seas and rivers, and worn away by glaciers, wind, and storms.

Into this climate of ideas came Charles Darwin. Much of what he was to "discover" had already been expressed before him, but not in exactly the way he did. In one sense what he achieved was not entirely new. Yet in another sense it was new, because no one had put together the several different and quite separate ideas of the day into a general theory that not only saw *evolution* as the origin of the species, but included a reasonable *cause* of the process as well.

Charles Darwin was the son of a successful and somewhat stern physician in the English cathedral town of Shrewsbury. He was interested in the study of nature from an early age, but his main passion was hunting, fishing, and other outdoor sports. Coming from a well-to-do family, and lacking any strong conviction about his life's occupation, he could easily have become a sportsman and devoted his life to unproductive leisure. His father, however, urged Charles to study medicine, and lacking any strong reason not to, he entered Edinburgh University in 1825 for that purpose. Although he liked the courses in anatomy and physiology, he found when he first entered the operating room and saw blood and living flesh that he became very ill. For this reason he decided to give up medicine.

His father now suggested he study for the ministry and, seeing some attraction in the life of a village parson, young Charles next agreed on this course and entered Cambridge University in 1828. He found most of his classes and formal lectures dull and considered them wasted time. In his spare time he collected specimens of plants and animals, but without much sense of purpose because the collections served no basic scientific problem, other than idle curiosity and his general love of nature.

About this time Darwin developed a new friendship that was to focus his deeper interests and influence his later life. The new friend was Henslow, the professor of botany. He must have seen something unusual in Darwin. They were together on regular class field trips, and at many other times as well, including long walks in the country around Cambridge and visits in Henslow's home.

It was Henslow who provided the opportunity that changed Darwin's whole life by recommending him to Captain Robert Fitzroy of H.M.S. *Beagle*. This ship, under Fitzroy's command, was to resume the British Admiralty's project of surveying the coastline of South America. Fitzroy thought his ship's company should include a naturalist who could take advantage of the many rich opportunities for geological and biological observations during the voyage. The opportunities of this voy-

H.M.S. *Beagle*

age for following his scientific interest were more than Darwin could resist, and in September of 1831 he signed on with Captain Fitzroy after he and his uncle had overcome the violent objections of his father.

The *Beagle*, a square-rigged Navy brig of ten guns, sailed from England in December, 1831, on a voyage that was to have lasted two or three years, but went on for five. For Darwin these five years were his real education. They were one long laboratory experiment during which he rapidly grew into a mature naturalist.

He had taken with him on the voyage Charles Lyell's great book, *The Principles of Geology*, which he read and reread in that first year out. Lyell recognized that rocks are still being formed then destroyed by glaciers and erosion. He saw that ancient geologic times were really like ours. Such evidence demolished the catastrophic idea of creation. This book gave Darwin the basis for understanding his own observations of volcanic craters in the Galapagos Islands, glaciers coming down to the sea in Tierra del Fuego, and coral reef formation in the Keeling Islands of the Pacific.

Almost everything he saw on the voyage suggested to him the idea of evolution. The fossil tooth of a horse found in South America and fossil bones in Patagonia, set him to thinking about the problem of extinction of earlier living species and about the links between species now alive and those extinct. This caused him to wonder how the changes from species to species had come about.

In the Galapagos Archipelago he was impressed by the variety of birds and the differences among them on neighboring islands. Although on each of these islands the birds had special differences, they resembled those he had seen on the American mainland. This made him think they all must have come from the same common mainland ancestor. From this observation he began to develop theories about what happens to animal species that are isolated from others. What changes — if any — take place in them over the years, and how do these differences between the species result from the adaptation of each one to his new environment?

Home again in 1836, Darwin returned to Cambridge where he began the long job of cataloguing his collection of specimens from the *Beagle*. The voyage had ruined forever any further thoughts he might have had toward the ministry. Because of his wealth, inherited from his father, he decided to settle down to a private life devoted to science.

Within a year after the return of the *Beagle* he completed an account of the voyage, and this was published

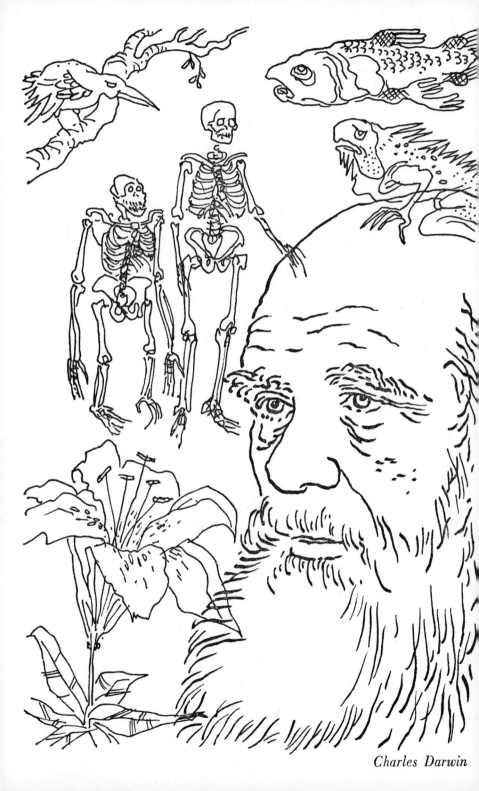

Charles Darwin

as part of Fitzroy's long and technical report. No wonder it drew almost no public notice. Later, however, it was published as a separate book, *A Naturalist's Voyage Round the World*, which attracted wide public attention.

Soon Darwin moved to London and continued his work there for the next four years. He became a close friend and pupil of Lyell's, and now his major interest was geology. He turned to a study of coral reefs, glaciers, and other geological problems that had arisen from his observations during the voyage. What had happened to his ideas about evolution of living species? They were still there, being turned over in his mind, forming slowly as he catalogued his collections and wrote of other things.

In 1839 he married his cousin, Emma Wedgwood, and soon afterward his health failed. This once rugged man now found his ability to do concentrated mental work sharply limited, and his former love of poetry and music gone. This strange change in his personality left his mind, as he described it, "a kind of machine for grinding general laws out of large collections of facts."

This illness finally forced him to find a quieter life than London offered, so in 1842 he and his family moved to a large country house on eighteen acres of secluded land near the Kentish village of Down. There he spent the rest of his life, seeing almost no one except his immediate family and a few close friends, following an exact daily routine of rest, walks, and work. Nothing is more remarkable than the amount of work he was able to accomplish with the restrictions his illness forced on him. The secret was his capacity for intense concentration for short periods of time, the regularity of his work habits, and his complete isolation from anything that might have distracted him.

With the completion of these geological studies Darwin next turned his whole attention to the problem of the species. He was now convinced that as the earth had gradually evolved by a natural process, so animals had evolved — and continued to evolve — by some natural process he could not yet clearly see. He first asked, "What is a species?" He could see clear differences between lions, whales, and dogs, but were there finer differences within these separate forms? He decided to pick one form, generally thought of as a separate species, and study it. For this he chose barnacles. He dissected them on a window table in his study, classified them, and made detailed descriptions of as many varieties as he could locate. From these studies on barnacles he saw evidence of special changes in the separate varieties, but a common set of characteristics that made them all one species.

Now at last he was ready to return to his notebooks and specimens from the *Beagle* voyage where his evolutionary theory began to grow. Nothing could explain the origin of separate species better than their descent from some common ancestor. During evolution each species developed its own body structure and behavior that it needed in order to survive in its changing environment.

Over the next year Darwin continued to experiment, describe, classify, read, and discuss ideas through a vast correspondence with anybody and everybody who might

have some useful information about the subject. He turned his attention to animal breeders, and learned as much as he could about their methods and results. He saw more clearly than ever a similarity between the way they artificially bred domestic animals to select and develop some desirable characteristic, and the way nature does the same thing more slowly over thousands of years, selecting certain characteristics that must be developed if the animal is to survive in its natural environment. This study strengthened his growing conviction that the natural evolution of species occurs by a slow, slow process of *natural selection* comparable to *artificial selection* practiced by these breeders of domestic animals.

So far so good, but what is the *cause* of this natural selection process? Darwin couldn't find the key to it in nature. How does nature do the selecting? What performs the role of the breeder? He thought about this for a long time; then one day in 1838 he happened to read an *Essay on Population* by the Reverend T. R. Malthus, a writer on economic and mathematical subjects. The times in England were influenced by visions of unlimited expansion of business and population. Malthus, however, was worried about the future effects of this expansion. What would finally limit the number of people the world could support? He saw that a point would be reached where population would outstrip the supply of food, and at this point nature, through a process of sheer want aided by disease and man's own wars, would place checks on further population growth. Such checks, Malthus saw as necessary if man is to avoid poverty and misery in his stay on earth.

This essay struck Darwin like a thunderbolt; in it he saw the key to his theory of natural selection. Nature must impose similar "checks" on the unlimited expansion of animal and plant populations, but what is it that determines which species are selected to survive? It must be those with characteristics that fit them best to survive in their environment; others unfitted for survival die out and become extinct. So, he thought, the cause of natural selection is the survival of the fittest; the counterpart of the artificial selection by the breeder on the farm.

Many of these ideas were known and discussed by biologists in Darwin's time, and before, but no one had seen their connections in just this way until Darwin put evolution, natural selection and its cause — survival of the fittest — into one single theory.

Although Darwin read Malthus's *Essay* in 1838, just two years after the return of the *Beagle*, he was not yet ready to publish his theory for the public. His plan was to write a huge and detailed book that would represent his lifetime's work, and present much evidence to support his theory. He was in no hurry, even though his friends Lyell and Hooker, the botanist, urged him to publish lest someone else with the same theory beat him to the draw. But Darwin was a careful worker and not to be hurried. He wanted all possible flaws in the theory examined and decided by the scientific evidence; moreover, he was well aware of the storm of controversy his theory would probably blow up. So he continued his painstaking work of a few hours each day in seclusion at Down for another twenty years!

Then one day in June, 1858, these timeless labors were rudely broken by a letter from far-off southeast Asia. It was from another English naturalist, Alfred Russel Wallace, and contained his new article entitled "Essay on the Tendency of Varieties to Depart Indefinitely from the Original Type." Darwin read it with amazement and alarm; here was his theory in the exact same form, complete, and supported by good evidence! Wallace had been studying the geology and living forms of the Malay Archipelago. He had also seen the similarity between artificial selection, in domestic breeding of species, and the process of natural selection, and like Darwin had used this as the basis for a theory of evolution. He had also read Malthus and from his *Essay* developed the same idea of survival of the fittest as the cause of natural selection! Wallace's observations were much fewer than Darwin's, and rather than a large book he had produced a shorter essay. He recognized Darwin as the master in the field, and for this reason had sent him the essay for his criticisms and suggestions before publishing.

Wallace's essay was a heavy blow to Darwin. Although practically retired from the world and remaining outside the professional scientific societies of his day, Darwin still hoped for fame. In his deep discouragement his first impulse was to abandon the ambitious plans for his large book and arrange for publication of Wallace's essay. But he asked Lyell and Hooker what they thought best. He decided to make a joint presentation — before the Linnean Society of London — of Wallace's essay and parts of his own work. This presentation — one of the most important in the history of ideas — was made on July 1, 1858. Like so many important events that appear ahead of their time, it had no apparent effect on the learned audience that heard it. They were unconvinced and left the meeting with the same traditional views of creation with which they had come.

Darwin now changed his own plans for the book. He abandoned the idea of writing so large a work, and decided instead on a shorter book of about five hundred pages to be published for the general public. This work took him the next thirteen months of intense labor to complete, and it appeared in November, 1859, with the rather heavy title: *On the Origin of Species by Means of Natural Selection, or the Preservation of Favoured Races in the Struggle for Life.* Now, however, we never use this long title; we just call it *The Origin of Species.*

The first edition was sold out on the day of publication, and by 1876 some sixteen thousand copies had been sold in England alone. It was soon translated into the major languages of the world. It was successful because England was ready for it; the ideas it expressed were in the air, and thinking people were ready to have their traditional views of the creation of the earth and the origin of man challenged. *The Origin of Species* did this. Its style of writing was interesting and a large public found it fascinating reading.

The storm of controversy that was expected was not

long in breaking, but Darwin stayed out of it at Down.
As a real scientist who respects the truth as he sees it, he
refused to change his views even though they were tremendously unpopular, especially with the Church.
Since he was shy and a poor debater, he let his support-
ers, like Thomas Huxley and Hooker, carry on the public argument.

The intensity of this argument is now a part of the
record of history. Seldom has a discovery of science had
such impact on public opinion. The debate between
Thomas Huxley and Bishop Wilberforce will never be
forgotten. To this day teaching theories of evolution is
forbidden by law in the schools of at least one state.
Even the famous trial of the schoolteacher Thomas
Scopes, in Dayton, Tennessee, in July, 1925 — that
brought together Clarence Darrow and William Jen-
nings Bryan as opposing lawyers, and resulted in the
conviction of the courageous Mr. Scopes — failed to
settle the dust.

Darwin's ideas and their later modifications have
taken their place alongside a series of other world-
shaking ideas, such as the genetics of Mendel, Einstein's theory of relativity, and Freud's discovery of psychoanalysis, that have emerged in the last one hundred
years. Today these ideas do not create a storm of debate;
the conflict between Science and the Church is largely
resolved in most places, and reasonable men see nothing
basically incompatible between a modern religious belief and theories of evolution.

Darwin lived on for twenty-three long, productive
years after *The Origin* first appeared, and turned his at-

tention to other things, like *Fertilization of Orchids, Expression of the Emotions, Climbing Plants, Different Forms of Flowers,* and *The Power of Movement in Plants,* just to name a few. Books on these and other subjects continued to appear right up until the year before his death. Many of these were the result of the simple imaginative experiments he performed in his study and gardens at Down; some are considered even finer scientific work than *The Origin.*

Yet *The Origin* stands as the cornerstone of Darwin's life. In the years after its first edition, Darwin continued to work on it and kept an open mind that allowed him to modify the original ideas through six subsequent editions of the book. His early theories of natural selection and survival of the fittest have changed some in the light of later scientific research, but the basic ideas remain. He gave the world a theory of the broadest general significance on which we continue to build toward a more perfect understanding of who we are, and how we have reached our present form.

VII   An Individual Makes
the Discovery

THE DISCOVERER of penicillin was Sir Alexander Fleming, a shy, quiet, hard-working, and completely honest Scotsman who died at the age of seventy-four in 1955. By then his name was known all over the world and wherever he went he was treated like a movie celebrity. Yet the man and the circumstances that led to his great discovery were far removed from this later life as a famous man. They were those of many long years of hard work in a small, poorly equipped laboratory where few knew of the work and almost no one recognized its importance for nearly a decade after it appeared.

Chance also played a big part in the penicillin story at several important points along the way, but these gifts of chance were recognized by a mind prepared to see them when they appeared. Penicillin is one of our finest examples of how the cooperative efforts of a team later exploit and develop a discovery — carried as far as the discoverer could carry it — and then give it to the world in its finished, most useful form. Let's see how all this happened.

Fleming came to London as a young man from the small family farm in Scotland. As a boy he had learned to love nature and to see everything in his surroundings. Not much escaped his searching eye on the four-mile walks from the farm to the one-room schoolhouse in the village of Darvel. So it wasn't strange that he should be satisfied only for a short time to work as a clerk in a London office, and sought instead an education as a Doctor of Medicine.

He received this education with brilliant success at St. Mary's Hospital Medical School in London, the same school where he also took his internship and surgical training and where he spent the rest of his life as teacher and research worker. He was headed for a career in surgery when the first of a series of unplanned chances came along and turned him into the path that led to penicillin.

One of the most brilliant members of the staff at St. Mary's in those days was Dr. Almroth Wright, who had established an inoculation service which operated as a separate department of the medical school, doing research in vaccines and producing them for treatment of certain diseases. Dr. Wright was an enthusiastic hunter, a good shot, and he wanted to add some new members to the St. Mary's Rifle Club. This club had recently lost the rifle competition between the London medical schools, and Freeman, one of Wright's young associates, was anxious to improve it. When he asked if anyone knew of good shots among the resident staff of doctors, someone recommended Fleming, who had shown his skill with a rifle in the hospital's drill team. Freeman was told that Fleming was a surgeon and that he would be leaving the hospital after completion of his training. Freeman conceived the idea of getting Fleming a job on Wright's inoculation service so that St. Mary's could keep him for the rifle team. Wright took him on, after Freeman had convinced Fleming that the job would tide him over while he looked for a good position in surgery. But Fleming never went back to surgery. He stayed on in what seemed to him a secure and possibly interesting position working with microbes about which he knew very little. So, because he was a good rifle shot, the young surgeon became a microbiologist and entered a laboratory. There he would find an association with Almroth Wright that would provide the training he needed and at the same time prepare his mind to recognize the significance of the chance observation that led to penicillin twenty-three years later.

Vaccination and other forms of inoculation protect against disease by imitating in a less dangerous way what nature does with the disease itself. The germs, or microbes, when killed or weakened and injected into the body, stimulate the body's tissues to make the same protective antibodies that are made during the disease itself. Wright believed that all infectious diseases — those caused by microbes — would one day be conquered by such inoculations. This was to him a beautiful example of working with nature to stimulate her own disease-protecting processes, and Wright fired up all his associates in the laboratory with this philosophy.

At about this same time in Germany, however, Paul Ehrlich achieved a brilliant success with his discovery of the chemical compound of arsenic which he called *salvarsan*, and showed it to be a powerful killer of the

Dr. Fleming

microbe that causes syphilis. This discovery gave birth to the field called *chemotheraphy*, or the treatment of disease with chemicals made artificially by man in the laboratory.

Fleming's imagination was fired by the possibilities of controlling microbial diseases by such chemicals, each designed to kill a specific microbe or group of them. Yet Almroth Wright, his teacher whom he respected greatly, continued to argue that chemotherapy could not hope to achieve what nature's own chemicals, the antibodies, could do in the control of infectious diseases.

Out of these two influences there seems to have grown in Fleming's mind a belief that living things pro-

Dr. Ehrlich

duce a host of chemicals, more than just the specific antibodies, that protect the organism against disease-producing microbes. The great French microbiologist Louis Pasteur had noticed that some bacteria kill others off when the two are injected together in an animal. Such an effect would mean that the one microbe produces some chemical which kills the other microbe. Such a substance would be called an *antibiotic*, meaning "against life." Fleming wondered whether Pasteur's observation might be but an example of a much broader process of antibiotic protection that might even include man. Do man's own tissues naturally make antibiotic substances that protect his organs from the invasion of microbes at all times?

One day in 1922 Fleming was looking at some bacteria growing in a culture dish containing agar. The bacteria grow on the agar, and these had grown from some mucus that Fleming had taken from his own nose — because he had a cold — and placed on the agar. While he looked at this dish he noticed something very interesting. Immediately surrounding the place where he had planted the mucus there were no bacteria growing, the agar surface was clear; further out the growth was abnormal and weak. Only far out around the edges of the agar surface was there normal heavy bacterial growth.

Fleming became very excited, because this observation suggested to him that the mucus from his nose contained not only bacteria, but some substance that also kills bacteria! Could it be one of his natural antibiotics?

Feverishly he repeated the experiment and noticed the

same thing. He went on to find that when he added a small amount of mucus to a test-tube broth culture, cloudy with a heavy growth of bacteria, the broth became clear in just a few minutes! Whatever it was in the mucus not only killed the bacteria, but dissolved them as well.

Fleming started to look for this substance in other secretions that moisten exposed parts of the body, as mucus does the lining of the nose, and so he next tried tears. He and his assistant sucked lemons and collected their tears. When tear fluid was streaked on a plate of growing microbes or added to a cloudy broth culture, the microbes were dissolved more powerfully than they had been with mucus. Fleming next tried tears with a whole variety of microbes, and found that the tears dissolved some of them, but not others. These observations suggested to him that organs might secrete substances that protect them from some diseases. He thought that perhaps disease results from those microbes that are not destroyed by the body's own antibiotics. Fleming named this first discovered antibiotic that exists in nose mucus and tears, *lysozyme* because it causes microbe *lysis*, which means dissolving. The *-zyme* part of the word came from his belief that the substance belongs to a class of living chemicals called *enzymes*. Lysozyme has now been shown to exist in the secretions of many living forms.

With this background of experience with lysozyme, it was quite natural that Fleming should have discovered penicillin seven years later, in 1929. The circumstances and the observation were in many ways quite similar, and the lysozyme experience had made him ready to make such a discovery.

Fleming was always careful not to throw away his culture dishes or tubes right away, and he used to warn his students in the laboratory to keep their cultures around for some time and observe the bacterial growth on them from time to time. "Who knows," he would say, "you might just see something you hadn't recognized before."

His small, crowded laboratory had a window that looked out on Praed Street behind St. Mary's Medical School, and his culture dishes with their bacteria growing on agar were piled on the laboratory bench beside the open window. Standing beside this window, Fleming would lift the glass cover off his petri-dish cultures, and for a moment look at the round colonies of bacteria on the agar, noting their size, color, texture, and whether they looked alike or different; all things that told him something about the nature of the bacteria he was studying.

If the microbiologist is to grow his bacteria this way, in "pure culture" with only one kind of bacteria on the culture medium, he must be very careful that other bacteria or molds don't get on the plate or in the broth and contaminate the pure culture. Microbiologists worry a lot about these contaminants, and go to much trouble to avoid them.

One day in 1928 a colleague of Fleming's — named Pryce — went to see him in his laboratory, and found him looking at some colonies of a yellow *staphylococcus* in his agar cultures. When he lifted the cover off one

petri dish he found that it had become contaminated by
the growth of a mold such as gets on old bread or fruit.
This mold had probably come in the open window from
Praed Street and now grew on the nourishing agar as a
round, soft, felt-like mat. Immediately Fleming noticed
an interesting thing, and pointed it out to Pryce. In the
area just surrounding the mold there were no colonies of
staphylococci growing. This looked like lysozyme
again, only this time it was a mold instead of mucus or
tears. Was the mold producing an antibiotic that
diffused for some distance into the agar and killed the
bacteria or stopped their growth?

Fleming acted at once. He kept the petri dish, but before putting it aside, he transplanted, with a fine wire
loop, some of the spores of the mold to another sterile
agar plate and incubated it at room temperature for several days until he had another soft round growth of mold
on the agar. Now he transferred to the agar, one at a time,
several different kinds of bacteria, streaking them out in
spoke-like lines from the mold colony in the middle of
the plate. The dish was then covered and incubated
overnight. Next day the bacteria were growing in separate straight bands radiating out from the mold. Fleming noticed to his delight that some of the bacteria grew
up to within a certain distance of the edge of the mold
then stopped, while others grew right up to the mold.
This meant to him that some kinds of bacteria were
killed by the mold while others were not.

What further delighted Fleming was that some of
those killed by the mold were disease producers; so the
antibiotic being produced by the mold was unlike lyso-

zyme; it killed the disease producers, and so might possibly be used in the treatment of human disease. Fleming saw this possibility at once.

He now grew the mold in a richly nourishing broth, and noticed as the thick mat of mold grew on the surface that the broth under the mold turned a straw-yellow color. He then made culture plates in which he hollowed out a gutter running across the agar, and filled this gutter with some of this straw-colored fluid. Different bacteria were then streaked from the edge of the agar up to the gutter and the plate was incubated. The same thing happened as with the whole mold: some bacteria stopped growing at a distance from the gutter; others grew heavily right up to its edge.

In this way Fleming proved beyond doubt that the mold produces some chemical that diffuses out from the mold for some distance through the agar and either kills some kinds of bacteria or stops their growth in the agar containing it. He also realized with much excitement that if he could produce large quantities of this "mold juice" it might prove to be a miraculous cure for certain bacteria-produced (infectious) diseases — such as blood poisoning — that were almost always fatal to man. Fleming looked at the mold under the microscope, recognized it as a variety of common bread mold belonging to the family *Penicillium*, so he named his new antibiotic in the mold juice "penicillin."

Fleming was now anxious to isolate the penicillin from the mold juice, obtain it as pure crystals, and collect enough to test whether it would hurt animals and man and whether it would really cure infectious diseases as dramatically as it killed the bacteria on the culture plate. But Fleming was not a chemist and didn't know how to go about isolating the pure substance. What's more, he couldn't seem to interest any chemist in working with him.

Curiously, when he announced his discovery to the Medical Research Club in London in February, 1929, there were no questions asked and no discussion. No one was apparently impressed enough to realize what had happened, and this lack of interest was to last about another six years!

But Fleming didn't lose faith. He remained convinced that he had discovered something of the greatest importance to mankind, and he knew that sooner or later someone would come along with the chemical skill to isolate the new antibiotic free of the mold juice impurities that would make it dangerous to inject into man. Fleming's hope would come true, but not for another six years.

At this time there were two young doctors in the laboratory, Ridley and Craddock. Ridley had purified lysozyme for Fleming some years earlier, and now Fleming asked him to have a try at penicillin in association with Craddock. The two agreed to try, although they considered themselves poorly qualified for the job. Nevertheless they set up their equipment in an old narrow corridor of St. Mary's and went to work. Their method was to evaporate most of the water from the mold juice given them by Fleming, and in this way they hoped to concentrate the active penicillin enough so it would form crystals which could then be separated and dried. Since

Drs. Ridley and Craddock

they knew that the penicillin was destroyed by heat, they had to evaporate the water by creating a vacuum in the flask, and this they did with a pump. Try as they might all they got, when they evaporated the juice as much as they could, was a thick brown syrup. True, this contained the penicillin in some ten to fifty times more active form than in the original juice, but they could not make the crystals form, and after a few days the activity of the penicillin in the syrup disappeared.

In the light of later experience, we can see that Ridley and Craddock had come within a few steps of success. But they had gone about as far as their knowledge and equipment would lead them, and they had to abandon further attempts.

So Fleming's work as an individual was done. He had gone as far as he could with his knowledge and laboratory equipment. He continued to work on other aspects of penicillin for another twenty years, but it was now up to others to make the large effort necessary to prepare penicillin in pure form, test it for any poisonous effects in animals and man, and finally make it in large enough quantities for use in the treatment of human infectious disease. All these things were to be achieved with brilliant success, but not by one man alone. They required the combined efforts of a team with the necessary skills and facilities to do the job. In this phase many persons were to be involved, in Britain, the United States, and other countries, and the mighty resources of industry were finally included to complete the job. The two men, however, who played the main roles in this new team effort were Drs. Florey and Chain at Oxford University.

With them Fleming shared the Nobel Prize in medicine in 1945.

The original observation of the mold-contaminated plate that meant "penicillin" to Fleming took place in 1928 and was reported to the public in 1929. Although the importance of this observation went unnoticed for almost ten years, the solitary individual who made it was finally recognized and lifted to the very summit of fame through every honor and public tribute possible. The point to remember about Fleming is that his discovery, although in a sense made by chance, came from the eye and mind prepared by long practice at accurate observation. The discovery came from the mind that had formed an idea as the result of long thought, and an idea that let the man see lysozyme first and thus prepared him to recognize penicillin when he saw it later by chance. I wonder if it really was all pure chance after all?

VIII   A Team Completes the Job

For almost ten years after Fleming announced its discovery penicillin went unnoticed, and it appeared that it might be forgotten. But Fleming never gave up hope. What was needed now was the effort of a large team of people with a variety of skills, who could isolate the pure substance free from mold juice impurities, and then produce it in large enough quantities so they could determine its chemical structure. It could then be tested in animals for any poisonous side effects, and, after that, for its ability to cure infectious diseases. This would all lead finally to its testing in actual cases of human infection. If all this research proved that pure penicillin was the wonder drug it promised to be, then industry would have to be persuaded to undertake its mass production.

These developments began at Oxford University in 1935. Dr. Howard Florey, an Australian, had been appointed to the professorship of pathology in the beautiful new Sir William Dunn Institute of Pathology at Oxford. He was fascinated with Fleming's discovery of lysozyme and decided to work on it. In the Dunn Institute there were divisions for bacteriology and biochemistry, as well as pathology, and Florey was gathering a

staff to man these areas. Sir Frederick Gowland Hopkins — the discoverer of vitamins — was then professor of biochemistry at Cambridge University, and it was
natural that Florey should consult him in his search for
a bright young biochemist. Hopkins recommended to
Florey a person whom he thought had just the qualifica-
tions Florey wanted, Dr. E. B. Chain.

Chain had been born in Berlin of a German mother
and Russian father, and had received his graduate training in biochemistry at the University of Berlin. Because
he was a Jew, he had left Germany when Hitler and the
Nazis started the Jewish persecution; he had come to
England, working first at the University of London,
then at Cambridge. Florey offered him the job at Oxford
and Chain accepted with pleasure.

Florey suggested at first that Chain work on lysozyme; this interested Chain and he started in with vigor
and imagination using the purified lysozyme that a colleague of Florey's, Dr. Abraham, had made. Chain
thought, as Fleming had, that lysozyme was an *enzyme*,
and in his study he showed this to be true. He also discovered that lysozyme dissolves bacteria by splitting
apart their hard outer wall that is made of a substance
called *polysaccharide*, related chemically to sugars and
starches.

With the lysozyme research completed, Chain was
now ready to start on a new problem. He had become
deeply interested, as Florey was, in antibacterial substances. He and Florey talked a lot together about this
subject on long walks in the University Parks, and
Chain read deeply in the literature on it. During this

period he came across Fleming's 1929 pencillin article, and of all the things he read this interested him the most. He saw the efforts that Ridley and Craddock had made to isolate penicillin from the mold juice and noted their statements about its destruction by heat or just by standing for some time at room temperature. He became fascinated by the penicillin idea, and discussed it at length with Florey, who also became deeply interested in it.

Chain decided he wanted to go to work on penicillin and try to isolate it from the mold juice, hoping he could prepare it in pure crystalline form. Then he could determine its chemical structure and its action against microbial disease. Florey agreed.

Chain suggested they apply to the Rockefeller Foundation in New York for money to support their research and, again as chance would have it, the Foundation made them a grant of five thousand dollars — a ridiculously small sum when you think what came from the work it made possible.

Chain began his research early in 1939 not long before the outbreak of World War II. He obtained some spores of *Penicillium notatum* from a colleague in the Institute who had obtained some from Fleming for another purpose. Chain had to learn all about molds and how to grow them. He did this with his characteristic thoroughness and soon had good cultures growing without contaminants.

The program involved not only the isolation and purification of the penicillin, which would be Chain's particular interest, but the biological testing of the preparations in animals, and the provision of pure cultures of bacteria to test their effects outside the body. For this team approach the Dunn Institute was well suited. Chain would prepare pure penicillin and determine its chemical structure, and Florey would be in charge of all testing for poisonous side effects and experimental infections in animals.

After his experience with lysozyme, Chain started working with the belief that penicillin was also an enzyme. He therefore decided to handle the chemical isolation procedure as if he were extracting an enzyme from animal tissues. This meant very gentle handling; enzymes are proteins and are easily destroyed by acids, alkali, alcohol, or high temperature. He decided to use the freeze-drying technique for evaporating the water from the mold juice. This procedure had recently been invented and had proved successful in the preservation of human blood plasma.

In freeze-drying, the solution to be evaporated is frozen in a flask immersed in liquid air or dry ice while a vacuum is created in the flask by a strong vacuum pump that removes the air. When substances are frozen this way, the water of the solution passes directly from the solid to the gaseous state without becoming a liquid in between. This is how snow and ice are lost as vapor into the air on high, very cold mountaintops. In the process solid substances that were dissolved in the water before freezing keep their activity and are left behind when the water is removed.

When applied to the mold juice this method was immediately successful. Residues from freeze-dried juice consisted of a brownish powder with antibiotic activity many times greater than the original juice, but still not completely free of impurities.

In an attempt to get rid of these impurities Chain tried to dissolve the powder in something that would dissolve the penicillin without dissolving the impurities which he could then simply separate on filter paper in a funnel. Although he knew some alcohols were likely to destroy the penicillin if, as he thought, it was a protein enzyme, he nevertheless decided to try them. Ethyl alcohol didn't dissolve it, but to his surprise methyl alcohol did, and the impurities were left behind. He found to his further surprise that he could prevent the destruction of the penicillin in the alcohol if he quickly diluted it with a large volume of water, thus reducing the concentration of alcohol below the destructive level. Then all he had to do was remove the methyl alcohol and water by another bout of freeze-drying, and he was left with a fine bright-yellow powder, which on further purification showed penicillin activity some thousand times greater — on agar culture of bacteria — than Fleming's original mold juice.

Chain had by now been joined by Dr. Heatley, and together they worked hard and finally produced enough of the precious yellow powder so Florey could test its possible poisonous effects on animals. This was an important step in the research, because penicillin — or any other drug for that matter — can only be useful in treating human disease if it kills the microbes without hurting the man. Florey injected 25 milligrams into a mouse, a large dose for a small animal, and was delighted to see that it didn't hurt the mouse at all. Further samples of the precious substance confirmed this finding, so the stage was set to test its effect on an experimental bacterial infection in laboratory animals.

In May, 1940, just one month before the battle of Dunkirk, Florey injected a group of mice with three different types of bacteria, all killed by penicillin on the agar culture, and all producers of fatal infections in man. These bacteria were of the types known as *Staphylococci*, *Streptococci*, and *Clostridium* (this last the producer of dread gas gangrene). Twenty-five mice received the bacteria but no penicillin, and would serve as untreated controls. Twenty-five others received the bacteria plus penicillin injections at regular intervals.

Florey slept in the laboratory that night and was awakened every two hours by an assistant to observe his animals. Sixteen hours later *all* of the untreated mice were dead, but twenty-four of the twenty-five treated with the new purified penicillin were alive! This was nothing short of a miracle. The results were reported in the British medical journal *Lancet* on August 24, 1940, with the names of Florey, Chain, and Heatley as the authors.

Sir Alexander Fleming happened to read this article; it was the first he knew of the Oxford team's work, and he was very excited to learn of it. Here was the chemical isolation of penicillin he had so long hoped for, and that Ridley and Craddock had tried with such bad luck. Fleming decided to go up to Oxford and see the group. Chain was surprised to see him; he had thought Fleming was dead! From this visit there developed a close

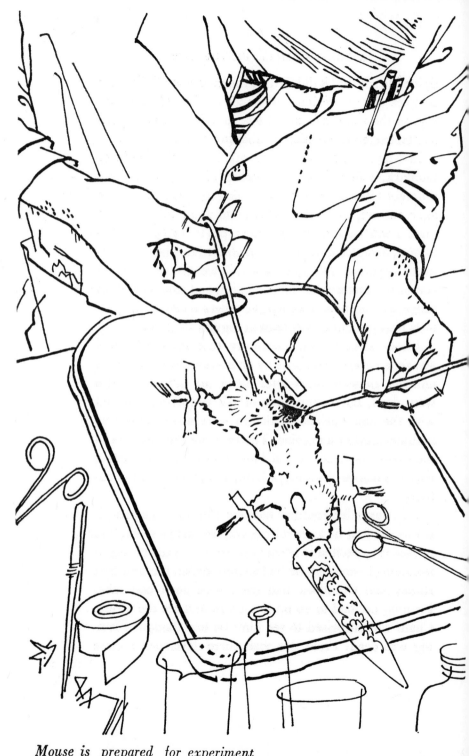

Mouse is prepared for experiment

relationship between Fleming and the Oxford workers; Fleming agreed to help them in any way he could and warmly encouraged their work.

Florey was now ready to treat a human case. Chain and Heatley went on preparing their powder, storing it up in the icebox against the day when a suitable case of an infectious disease presented itself. Soon that day arrived. In the hospital in Oxford there was a policeman dying from blood poisoning caused by the same staphylococcus given to the mice. Florey, Chain, and Heatley

Dr. Fleming

decided to use their precious supply of powder on this man, and in order to have its effect last for as long a period as possible they decided to give it by vein, letting the penicillin, dissolved in a weak salt solution, drip constantly into the vein. They weren't so worried about toxic side effects since they had seen how easily the mice had tolerated the drug. But they were worried that they might run out of their limited supply of the pure penicillin before the man was cured. The risk was worth taking, however, since the policeman was almost dead with boils all over his body and in his internal organs.

On February 12, 1941, they started treating the policeman. In twenty-four hours his condition had improved dramatically. He was taking food and his boils had started to clear up. But tragedy struck. They were running out of penicillin before the man would be cured! The agony of this knowledge was particularly hard since they knew the man could be cured if they could keep treating him. Heatley worked heroically to make more penicillin; he even collected the man's urine, extracted the penicillin excreted in it, and reinjected it into him. But all these efforts failed; the policeman's infection returned in full force and he died on March 15.

In spite of this setback the Oxford workers knew they had a miraculous drug and that they must push ahead. Hard work produced enough for further treatment of enough human cases so they knew beyond doubt that it was effective against certain microbe-produced diseases — effective beyond man's wildest dreams.

Now the time had come to produce the drug on a

large scale. Although Chain and Heatley were to set up a small industrial pilot plant at Oxford, the real needs for penicillin could only be met by the full resources of the chemical and drug industries. Florey decided to undertake the job of convincing industry to do it.

At this time Britain's situation was desperate. She was under constant attack from the air and the threat of German invasion. So it was understandable that the large British industries he approached said no. They were already completely committed to producing other goods vital to Britain's survival, and felt they couldn't take the risks involved in the big effort Florey asked of them. So Florey turned to America, and with Heatley left for New York in June, 1941, four months after the policeman's tragic death in Oxford. Florey took several strains of *Penicillium* mold with him.

Through a friend in New York, Florey was directed to Dr. Charles Thom, the man who had correctly identified Fleming's original mold as *Penicillium notatum.* Dr. Thom was now head of a mold section at the Northern Regional Research Laboratory at Peoria, Illinois. This laboratory had been recently established by the U.S. Department of Agriculture to find uses for the large quantities of agricultural waste products being dumped into the rivers of the Midwest.

Florey went around the laboratory talking to each scientist and finally came to Dr. Coghill who was head of the Division of Fermentation. They discussed the problem Florey had in mind: to discover ways to make molds produce more penicillin. Coghill believed he could help by finding new culture media for the mold to grow on and by searching for different strains of mold, the way farmers develop breeds of cattle for better milk or beef production.

As a by-product of starch production from corn there is a richly nutrient fluid produced called corn steep liquor. The fermentation laboratory had been trying to turn this "waste product" into something useful. A mold related to *Penicillium notatum*, Fleming's strain, and called *Penicillium chrysogenum*, was being grown in the corn steep liquor in an attempt to convert the glucose it contains into a related chemical called gluconic acid. The Peoria scientists thought it might be a good idea to grow some of the *Penicillium notatum* spores Florey and Heatley had brought in some of their corn steep liquor and see what it did to the penicillin production from the mold. To their delight it increased it tremendously. They then found quite by chance that if they added lactose, or milk sugar, the penicillin production went even higher.

Stimulated by these findings they began a search for new strains of mold. Word went out to scientists all over the world to send in mold samples, and the Army Air Force was enlisted to bring these samples to Peoria. In addition there were some girls working in the laboratory whose job was to shop in Peoria markets for moldy fruit and vegetables and bring them back to the scientists. One of these girls, named Mary, became known as "Moldy Mary." One day she returned with a moldy cantaloupe from which was isolated a mold spore belonging to the type *Penicillium chrysogenum*. This turned out to be an even greater penicillin producer when grown in

the lactose-corn steep liquor than the original *Penicillium notatum* Fleming had used. The strain was purified by the genetic methods of selective breeding, and to this day most of the mold strains producing the world's penicillin are descended from that moldy cantaloupe bought in the Peoria market. These improvements in mold strain and cultivation produced a penicillin which, when purified by Chain and Heatley's methods, was a million times more active than Fleming's original mold juice!

While all this success was being achieved by the group in Peoria, Florey had left on a trip around the United States and was having a different kind of success. He visited many chemical and drug producers and tried to persuade them to produce penicillin in large quantities. This meant building huge fermentation vats for growing *Penicillium* mold in thousand-gallon quantities, then designing and setting up the complicated apparatus for isolation and purification from the mold juice of the penicillin, adapting Chain and Heatley's methods to mass-production. Complicating all this was the necessity to do everything under sterile conditions to prevent the great mold culture vats and the purification process from becoming contaminated.

As may be imagined this would mean an enormous money investment for a company. The industrialists were also quick to recognize that some bright chemist would probably soon determine the structure of the penicillin molecule — indeed, Chain was already at work on it — and this discovery would surely mean the development of a chemical means of making penicillin. This would then mean the mold method would become obsolete, and the industries would see all their investment in this method of production lost.

For these reasons it is easy to see why the industrialists were not too sympathetic to Florey's pleas. However, he did have some success; two companies agreed to produce ten thousand liters of mold juice, and send the penicillin back to Oxford for testing.

At this time the need for an antibiotic like penicillin was great, and would become greater as America and Japan became involved in the World War and the number of casualties increased. One of the great killers in wars had always been the terrible battle wounds that become hopelessly infected. Fleming had worked on this problem in the First World War, and saw how ineffective were the usual methods of treating these infected wounds. The microbes from soil and dirty uniforms are blown into the depths of the wound and during the hours before the soldier can be taken to a place for treatment, the deadly microbes multiply and invade the body, producing a blood poisoning that is nearly always fatal. Penicillin had demonstrated ability to cure such cases, and Florey knew he must somehow persuade industry and government to make it in large amounts for distribution to the Armed Forces.

Before leaving the United States, Florey called on his old friend Dr. A. N. Richards, who had been professor of pharmacology at the University of Pennsylvania School of Medicine, and had recently been appointed by President Roosevelt to be president of the U.S. Government's powerful new Committee for Medical Research. This body had power in the government to push research and production of medical supplies to meet the needs of the war effort. Florey told Richards his story and impressed him with its urgency. Richards finally interested the U.S. Government in penicillin production, and the government, with war powers, soon started industry producing it.

During 1941 and 1942 production gradually increased, and a very carefully regulated clinical testing program was organized in the U.S.A. under the direction of Dr. Chester Keefer of Boston, and in Great Britain by a committee under the chairmanship of Sir Henry Dale. It was Dale who had earlier shared the Nobel Prize with Dr. Otto Loewi for the discovery of the transmitter substance, acetylcholine.

During this period of testing, the supplies of penicillin were small. Each case chosen for treatment around the country had to be carefully picked, and the procedure of treatment had to follow a general plan. Detailed records were kept on all these patients, and in this way a great deal was learned about how to use the drug properly. By 1943 large quantities of penicillin were available for treatment of the war wounded, and the number of lives saved by its merciful action was nothing short of miraculous.

In the years since its discovery by Fleming and its creation as a useful, life-saving drug by Florey, Chain, Heatley, and the host of others who made it possible, penicillin has become cheap and almost taken for granted. Many other antibiotics have been found in other molds and in bacteria of the soil. We have come to recognize that microbes can develop resistance to these antibiotics; indeed, this resistance can go so far that the microbe even reaches the point where it must have the antibiotic to grow! So we have learned that we mustn't use these wonder drugs of nature carelessly; we must use them only when they are needed and when we know the microbe causing the disease is killed by them — not all microbes are.

No matter how many new antibiotics are found in the future, penicillin will always occupy a special position of honor in medicine, just the way any "first" does — the way Roger Bannister does in sports because he was first to do the "impossible" and break the four-minute mile. Also, we can look for a long time in the history of medical research, and we won't find a better example than the penicillin story of the place in research of the individual and the team. Dr. Chain wrote: "The work of a team is important for the development of an idea already formulated, but I do not believe that a team has ever produced a new idea."

IX What A Good Idea Can Do

Since greek times men have known the disease we call "sugar diabetes." The very word comes from the Greek *dia* and *betio*, meaning to flow through a funnel, and refers to the large flow of urine that sufferers from this disease have. The whole name of the disease is *Diabetes mellitus*. *Mellitus* means "honey," and is used here because the urine contains much sugar and seemed like honey to some early doctor.

In this disease sugar, or more accurately glucose, is not properly used by the body. The glucose piles up in the blood, spills through the kidney carrying abnormal amounts of water with it into the urine, and causes severe dehydration. When glucose is not properly used, fats aren't either, and incomplete combustion products of fats accumulate in the blood. These substances are acids and they get the diabetic in trouble. High blood-glucose levels, as such, don't hurt him.

Over the years there grew much speculation about the cause of this disease, but it always kept pointing to the pancreas as the site of the trouble. It wasn't known, however, whether in diabetes the pancreas failed to produce something necessary for the proper use of glucose, or produced something abnormal that blocked its normal use by the tissues.

This argument wasn't really settled until 1889, when von Mering and Minkowski, in Germany, showed that removal of the pancreas in dogs causes typical and permanent diabetes. The pancreas of calves is what we eat as "sweetbreads." It is a long, pinkish gland with a rounded head and a tapering tail lying across the spine just under the stomach. Most of its cells secrete digestive juices that are poured into the small intestine.

In 1869, Paul Langerhans, a medical student in Germany, described small "islands" of cells scattered through these digestive cells of the pancreas. These became known as the *islands* (or *islets*) *of Langerhans*, and it is now accepted that these cells secrete a chemical substance into the bloodstream; this was named *insulin* by its discoverers. It is the blood sugar-regulating "hormone" that is missing in *diabetes mellitus*. Let's look at the story of its discovery, and the avenues of understanding and benefit to man that were opened by it.

Following von Mering and Minkowski's pioneer work of producing experimental diabetes by removing the pancreas in dogs, a number of research workers tried to extract the pancreas and obtain the active substance. But when injected into animals the extracts either had no effect on the blood-sugar level or produced such poisonous effects that they were useless. In 1909 a German physician, Zuelzer, had treated five diabetic patients with a pressed juice of pancreas which was extracted with alcohol and evaporated to dryness. The powder that was left was then dissolved in a salt solution. When injected into these patients the excretion of sugar and the fat acids in the urine disappeared, and the patients' condition improved. All of them, however, had severe chills, fever, and some vomiting; this showed that there were still impurities in the pancreas powder. For some reason Zuelzer never continued his study, which was too bad because he was very close to the discovery of insulin that Dr. Frederick Banting would make with Charles Best in Toronto, Canada, thirteen years later.

Dr. Frederick G. Banting was born on a farm near Toronto on November 14, 1891. He might have become another farmer, but circumstance determined that he

Dr. Banting

should have a medical education at the University of Toronto, from which he graduated as a doctor in 1916. After service in the First World War, he returned to Canada, received further hospital training, and opened an office as a doctor in London, Ontario.

In those early months of practice there was very little business for the young Dr. Banting, and he found that he had a lot of time on his hands. So he decided to seek work in the local medical school of the University of Western Ontario, hoping to earn a little money and at the same time improve his mind. He was successful in obtaining a position as demonstrator in physiology, similar to an instructor in one of the universities in the United States. His duties were to assist in the teaching laboratories and give some lectures to the medical students in their course in physiology. While he was doing this, Banting planned a course of reading that would prepare him to take the examinations that would qualify him as a specialist in surgery.

Among the lectures Professor Miller asked Banting to give were several on the way the body handles starches and sugars — or carbohydrates. During his study for these lectures Banting became deeply interested in the problem of diabetes, and realized how very little was known about its cause and treatment. Diabetics with a severe form of the disease simply couldn't be treated, and like cases of blood poisoning before penicillin, they just became worse and died. As a boy he had seen this happen to a favorite aunt, and he had never forgotten it.

One evening during this period Banting was reading

an article in one of the surgical journals by a Dr. Moses Barron of the University of Minnesota. It told of things he had noticed in certain patients with stones in the duct of the pancreas. The duct is the tube that leads from the pancreas to the small intestine. He noted that when a stone obstructs this duct the cells of the pancreas degenerate and the whole organ shrivels up. This process takes about eight weeks. Of most interest to Banting was Dr. Barron's observation that these patients do not become diabetic until very late, after most of the digestive cells of the pancreas have already degenerated. Barron noticed, when he looked at the pancreases of these people under the microscope, that even though the digestive-juice secreting cells were gone, the cells of the islets of Langerhans still looked quite normal. He also noticed this same thing in dogs when he tied the pancreas duct — the islet cells were the last to degenerate, and not until this happened did diabetes appear. On the basis of these observations Barron suggested that the islet cells of Langerhans secrete the substance that regulates blood sugar and when they stop secreting it, diabetes appears.

Banting became very excited as he read this article, because he suddenly had a bright idea. Perhaps, he thought, earlier attempts to make extracts of the pancreas had failed because the extraction procedure had released digestive juices from the pancreatic cells, and these had digested the islet-cell substance before it could ever be isolated. Naturally, if this were so, such extracts would be completely inactive and would have no effect of lowering the blood sugar. What was needed, he thought, was to get rid of the digestive juice-secreting cells first without damaging the islet cells, then one ought to be able to extract from pure islet cells the active blood-sugar principle. Now, Banting thought, if Barron was right in his ideas, then his observation was the key that would unlock the door, and lead to the successful isolation of the magic blood-sugar substance from the pancreas.

Banting couldn't sleep. Why hadn't Barron himself gone on to this next step, and tried to extract the dog's degenerated pancreas some weeks after its duct had been tied off — but before it became diabetic? That pancreas should still contain lots of islet cells but very few digestive-juice cells. Barron apparently hadn't seen this possible extension of his studies. Banting decided he should try it, and lest he forget his idea, he got up out of bed late that night and wrote down in his notebook this statement: "Ligate the pancreatic duct of dogs. Wait six to eight weeks for degeneration. Remove the residue and extract." The word ligate means to tie off.

Next day Banting went to see Professor Miller and some of the other members of the department of physiology. He told them of his idea and asked what they thought about it. They all thought it was a good idea. Banting said he would like to work on it and asked Dr. Miller if he could have ten dogs, a place to work for about ten weeks, and somebody to help him. Miller replied that he didn't have the facilities, and also that neither he nor the other department members knew enough about carbohydrates to be of much help to Banting. He suggested that he should go to Toronto to do the work.

There the professor of physiology was the eminent Scotsman Dr. J. J. R. Macleod, who was an authority on carbohydrates, and Miller thought he could be of much more help. So Banting drove in his old Ford over the familiar roads to his old medical school and made an appointment with Macleod. This was in November, 1920.

Banting reports that this interview went very badly; he thought he hadn't presented his idea to Macleod very well. At any rate Macleod asked him what he — an inexperienced surgeon — hoped to accomplish by these experiments when so many eminent men had tried to extract the blood-sugar principle from pancreas and failed. No, Macleod was very discouraging and Banting returned to London, his mission a failure. He couldn't forget his idea, however; the more he thought about it the more he wanted to try it, and he made two more trips

back to Toronto. The second time Macleod again discouraged him, but the third time he agreed to give Banting a chance.

Banting wanted to remove the pancreas from the ten dogs right then so the degeneration of the digestive cells could be going on during the time he was back in London before moving to Toronto in May. Macleod persuaded him, however, to wait till he came before beginning any of the work; then he could be on hand to look after the operated dogs himself. Banting agreed that this was a good idea.

He started work in Toronto in May, 1921, after Macleod gave him ten dogs and a laboratory for eight weeks. Macleod thought he should have help from someone in the laboratory who knew about carbohydrates and how the body handles them. There were two good second-year students, C. H. Best and E. C. Noble, who had been working in the laboratory, and Macleod assigned them to help Banting during the eight weeks he was to be there. Best would help the first four weeks and Noble the second. As it turned out, Noble left before his turn came up, so Best helped the whole time.

Shortly after they were settled, Macleod left for a summer visit to Scotland. Banting and Best were given a place to keep the dogs, an operating room, and a laboratory where they could make their extracts and perform the sugar measurements on blood and urine samples. Several dogs were operated on and a tie (or ligature) placed around the pancreatic duct leading into the small intestine. These dogs recovered well from the operation; and while they were waiting for the pancre-

Mammalian Laboratory at University of Toronto

ases to degenerate, Banting and Best practiced on normal dogs the delicate operation of removing the pancreas. Some of these dogs, who would later be diabetic, would serve as test animals for the extracts that were to be made from the duct-tied animals.

By seven weeks a couple of the duct-ligated dogs were chloroformed, and it was found to Banting and Best's disappointment that the pancreases had not completely degenerated as they had hoped. They soon found that if they put two ties around the duct, the degeneration took place as Barron had seen it. So they reoperated all their dogs and put in the second ligature in each.

On the 27th of July, they had a good diabetic dog with its pancreas removed, and they decided to try an extract of one of the degenerated pancreases. This was removed from one of the duct-ligated dogs, ground up and added to about 100 cubic centimeters of salt solution. Five cubic centimeters of this were then injected into the diabetic dog. Blood samples were drawn from a vein every half hour for two hours, and analyzed for their glucose content. To their excited delight the blood glucose fell from 0.200 to 0.110 per cent in the two hours, and the dog's condition improved quite noticeably. So Banting and Best experienced success: they had demonstrated beyond doubt the blood sugar-lowering power of pancreas, when freed of the cells that produce the digestive juices that had probably been destroying the active substance.

These bright young men were able to repeat their experiment enough times to convince themselves of its truth. They also showed the active substance in extracts

of pancreas that had been previously exhausted of digestive enzymes by being forced to secrete continuously for
several hours. And they found the material in very active form in the pancreas of calves removed before birth
from cows about to be slaughtered.

Since the new hormone came from the islets of Langerhans, Banting and Best named it *insulin* from the
Latin word *insula*, meaning island.

By the end of August, Macleod returned from Scotland to be greeted by the successful experimentalists. In
the short period of eight weeks Banting and Best had
brilliantly achieved what they had set out to do, and in
their minds the discovery was complete. What now remained was to find a better source of insulin than dog
pancreas, and to purify it enough so it could safely be
tried on human cases of diabetes.

But Macleod would not accept Banting and Best's
word for it, he had to see the experiments for himself. So
more dogs were prepared and the experiments repeated
exactly as before. The results were the same, and Macleod was convinced of the discovery the two men had
made. How close he had come to discouraging Banting
from ever doing it!

Macleod believed in being a professor in the old German tradition; he was the head of the laboratory and
others were simply assistants, particularly two as young
and inexperienced as Banting and Best. So Macleod in-
sisted that he should make the public announcement of
insulin's discovery because it had come from *his* laboratory. This caused Banting and Best some sorrow and
real anger, but nevertheless the announcement came in

the form of a paper given at Atlantic City, New Jersey, in May 1922, at a meeting of the Association of American Physicians. The paper was called "The Effects Produced on Diabetes by Extracts of the Pancreas." Macleod read the paper, and although Banting and Best were listed among the several authors, they weren't even invited to the meeting because they weren't members of the Association.

This strange aspect of the story continued, for when the Nobel Prize was awarded in 1923 for the discovery of insulin, it went to Banting and Macleod; Best was not included, even though the discoverers of insulin are always thought of as Banting and Best. Perhaps we don't know all the circumstances, but it certainly seems that Best should have been included.

As with penicillin, the research now called for the isolation of pure insulin from the pancreatic extracts, its testing on human cases of diabetes, and its production in large amounts by industry.

It was later found that insulin could be extracted, and partially purified, from beef pancreas without previous ligation of the pancreatic duct. On January 11, 1922, the first human cases of diabetes were treated with these extracts at the Toronto General Hospital. The blood sugar fell just as it had in dogs, but there were still impurities in the extracts, and these patients developed some fever and great soreness where the injections were made.

Insulin purification work proceeded at a rapid pace during the next years. Dr. J. P. Collip in Toronto achieved a much purer form; then the work went ahead under Best's direction, and during the summer of 1922 he made enough highly purified insulin to show beyond doubt its value in treating diabetic patients. Subsequently the production was taken over on an industrial scale by the Eli Lilly Company of Indianapolis, who still manufacture most of it produced in the United States. Insulin was finally crystalized in 1928 by Harrington and Scott and shown to be a rather small protein molecule containing zinc. Its exact chemical structure remained a mystery for about thirty years until determined by Frederick Sanger at Cambridge University in England. He received the Nobel Prize in chemistry for this work in 1958. Now that we know its chemical structure the way is open to discover how to make insulin, and the day may soon come when we will not have to depend any longer on the pancreases from the slaughterhouse as our source of it, but can make it in the factory instead.

Insulin belongs to that group of chemicals in the body known as *hormones*. These substances are secreted by glands — pituitary, thyroid, parathyroid, adrenal, and sex glands — and carried by the blood to other parts of the body where they change the speed of some specific biological process. Insulin apparently doesn't change the rate of the chemical reactions that use glucose inside the cell; rather, it speeds the rate at which glucose enters certain kinds of cell, particularly the muscle of the skeleton and heart. *How* it does this we do not know, but the fact that it does it opens a new field of understanding in diabetes and means we have come a long way since Banting and Best's discovery back in 1921. Banting's beautiful idea set a whole field of research in motion and it will continue — with huge benefits to mankind — until we know how insulin and the other hormones work.

X   Good Methods Count

A GOOD PIECE of research must use methods of observation and measurement that are both accurate and specific. Sometimes a research problem is ruined by poor methods. Occasionally a new method is invented and it suddenly makes possible measurements that were previously impossible, or so difficult that they were impractical. Sometimes, also, methods that were designed to solve a particular problem turn out to be useful in many other areas of research. In this way the introduction of a new method can cause a real revolution in science. A good example of this was the introduction of a very simple technique of chemical analysis called *chromatography*.

The term comes from the two Greek words *chroma*, meaning color, and *graphein*, to write or draw. So the technique must have something to do with drawing colored things. Actually chromatography refers to a group of similar methods for separating mixtures of gases or chemicals dissolved in liquids. The name comes from the earliest use of the technique in 1903 by a Russian botanist, M. S. Tswett, who separated colored mixtures of pigments extracted from leaves.

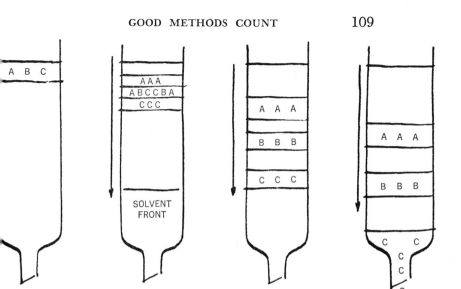

Tswett poured a petroleum-ether extract of the pigment of green leaves into a glass tube filled with powdered chalk. As the colored extract seeped down through the column of chalk the mixture of pigments separated into individual colored bands at different levels of the column. Thus Tswett had a colored drawing, or *chromatogram*, of these separate pigments in the mixture. He was then able to separate them by pushing the column of chalk out of its glass tube container and cutting each colored section into a separate fraction with a knife, as one would slice a loaf of bread. Then he could soak out each pigment from these separate chalk pieces and make the necessary chemical analyses on them to tell accurately what each pigment was. Although the term was applied originally to colored compounds, techniques of chromatography are used widely with colorless mixtures, but the original term remains in use.

For a long time chemists have separated the individual substances of a mixture by taking advantage of different degrees to which these components dissolve in different liquid solvents. For example, one substance in a mixture dissolves more easily in water, while another dissolves more easily in ether. So if a water solution of these two substances is shaken with ether, the second one will go into the ether and the first will stay in the water. Since water and ether don't mix, they can be separated as two layers, each carrying one of the two dissolved substances with it.

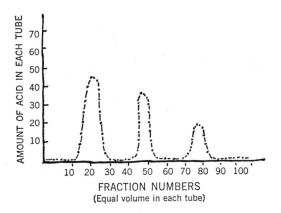

FRACTION NUMBERS
(Equal volume in each tube)

One form of chromatography takes advantage of this fact, and two Englishmen, Drs. A. J. P. Martin and R. L. M. Synge, were awarded the Nobel Prize in chemistry in 1952 for discovering it. In this form of chromatography two liquids bind to some solid substance such as powdered paper. The mixture of substances to be separated is then poured into the top of a glass tube filled with thin powdered paper that has been soaked

with the first liquid. This is similar to what Tswett did with his chalk column. The mixture containing the substances to be separated now seeps through the column, and some of the individual components of the mixture will dissolve in the liquid bound to the powdered paper, and some will pass on through the column with the liquid being poured through. In this way the components will be separated. By collecting separate samples of the fluid coming from the bottom of the glass column, these different substances can be caught separated from each other.

A similar form of this kind of chromatography was introduced in 1944 when Consden, Gordon, and Martin

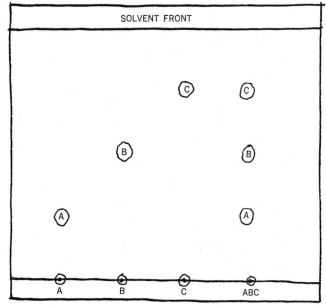

showed how simple strips of filter paper can be used — instead of a packed column — as the solid material. The mixture to be separated is placed as a spot on a line drawn across the paper a little bit above its bottom edge. The spot is allowed to dry, and the paper is hung in a closed jar with its bottom edge dipping in a trough containing some specially chosen liquid. The liquid then rises in the paper by capillary action, like coffee in a sugar cube, and as it does it drags the substances in the spot with it up into the paper. These substances are then held back by the paper to different degrees, and so they are separated on the paper as individual spots that can be developed, or seen, in a number of different ways.

This same thing can be done just in reverse. You can hang the edge of a strip of filter paper over a glass rod in a trough of the liquid set up in the top of the closed jar.

MIXTURE OF
COMPONENTS
PUT ON TOP OF
PAPER HERE

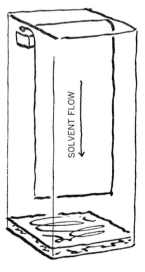

SOLVENT TROUGH
IN TOP OF JAR

PAPER HANGING
OVER GLASS ROD
INTO SOLVENT

SOLVENT FLOW

POOL OF SOLVENT
COLLECTED AFTER
DRIPPING OF BOTTOM
OF PAPER

The liquid then rises by capillary action into the paper, through the spots of mixture, then over the curve of the hanging paper and down. The moving liquid drips off the edge of the paper into the bottom of the jar. In this way a syphoning system is set up which keeps a continuous flow of the liquid moving down the paper, and the substances in the mixture of the spot move to different points down the paper and become separated. This is called *descending paper chromatography.*

One can also run a paper chromatogram in two directions with two different moving solvents, and separate many substances of a mixture that could not be separated if the chromatogram were run in just one direction. This technique has been very useful in showing the twenty-one separate amino acids that are the building blocks out of which our body's tissue proteins are made. In this type of chromatography the fluid containing the amino acids is spotted in one corner of a large square piece of filter paper and dried. Then the bottom edge of the paper is dipped in the first liquid, which is allowed to climb up the paper almost to the top by capillary action. Then the paper is removed, dried, and put back in the jar; only this time the other side of the paper is dipped into a second liquid in the bottom of the jar. This one then also rises up into the paper by capillary action in a direction at right angles to the first and separates the many amino acids even further than they were by the first movement of fluid in the paper.

In each of these ways of doing paper chromatography the separated substances of the mixture have to be identified on the paper after the run. This is done in a variety of ways after the paper has been dried. For instance, if the components of the mixture are acids or alkalis, the dried paper can be sprayed with some dye such as phenol red or bromcresol green, and the acid will show as a spot of one color against a background of another color. Acid spots on a paper sprayed with phenol red will appear as bright yellow against a red background. Amino acids separated from protein on the two-direction chromatogram turn a blue or purplish color when heated with a chemical called ninhydrin. So these paper chromatograms for amino acids are sprayed with ninhydrin and then placed in an oven. After a while the chemical reaction between amino acids and ninhydrin has taken place and the amino acid "map" now formed shows as neatly separated blue-purple spots on a white background.

Some substances fluoresce when ultraviolet light shines on them. Certain vitamins behave this way. On a dried paper chromatogram of these vitamins taken into a dark room and placed under an ultraviolet lamp, the spots will show plainly as a blue, yellow, or greenish fluorescence.

Sometimes we can use radioactivity to identify colorless spots on a paper chromatogram. The paper can be scanned by a Geiger counter which measures radioactivity. Over the invisible spot containing a radioactive substance the Geiger counter will start to make a rapid series of clicks.

Still another way to identify such radioactive spots is to put a photographic film on top of the paper chromatogram, allow enough time for the radioactivity to expose the film — the way light or X rays do — then develop the film. The spots will appear on the film corresponding to the spots on the paper.

There are endless ways to show where the spots are on chromatograms. I have discussed just a few of these. Unknown spots on a chromatogram are identified by comparing them with spots of known substances run on the paper in exactly the same way on control chromatograms. A certain substance will always move to exactly the same position on a paper chromatogram run with the same liquid under exactly the same conditions each time.

It is easy to see that this wonderfully simple method can be used not only to tell what different substances are in a mixture, but also how much of each one is there. Once formed on the paper, the spot containing all of a particular substance can be cut out with scissors, the substance in it soaked out of the paper, and its exact amount determined by some suitable chemical means.

There are other kinds of chromatography besides the type we have been discussing, and these have increased the usefulness of this method in research. One kind takes advantage of the fact that certain substances besides paper particles bind other substances to them. Finely powdered charcoal, chalk, or certain dried clays act in this way. When a mixture of substances in a solution is passed through a glass column containing one of these binding materials, some of the substances are bound to the particles more than others and so pass through the column more slowly. In this way the substances are separated. Suppose all the substances in a mixture are completely bound to powdered charcoal, but the bond of each one is broken by a different temperature. You can put the mixture of such substances on the top of the column and let it seep through the packed binding material. Now suppose all the substances are completely bound. You can now run through the column, one after another, liquids with different temperatures, and the individual components will be selectively unbound one by one, and appear one after the other in the samples of fluid collected from the bottom of the column. In such procedures separate solutions of different temperature can be put through the column one after the other, or things can be arranged so that the temperature of one solution changes continuously. This represents one of the most delicate refinements of the chromatographic technique.

Another type called *ion-exchange chromatography*, is similar to the type described above in its use of glass tube columns filled with small granules of evenly packed material, and the use of unbinding techniques. But the principle of the binding is different. Instead of whole molecules adhering to the binding substance in the column, it is electrically charged ions that do so. Acids, alkalis, and their salts when dissolved in water break apart — or dissociate — into electrically charged particles called *ions*. For example sodium chloride, represented chemically as $NaCl$, in water dissociates into positively charged sodium ions (Na^+) and negatively charged chloride ions (Cl^-).

Ion exchangers, such as the Permutit water softeners or several resins in current use, are granular substances of different sizes that can be evenly packed into glass columns like the binding particles we were just describing. Such columns of resin can then exchange their own bound ions with others for which they have greater electrical attraction in the mixture of dissociated substances percolating through the column. Here again special techniques are used to dissociate the ions from the resin one after another, and let them go out of the column at different rates separated from one another.

It is easy to see what a revolutionary effect these chromatographic techniques have had on research. It would take a whole library of books to tell about the many problems they have allowed research scientists to solve, but I would like to describe just a few as examples of how these techniques have been used.

Body proteins can be broken down into their amino acids by heating them with acid or treating them with digestive enzymes of the intestine juices. The individual amino acids in these mixtures can then be identified, as we have seen, by chromatography on paper or ion-exchange columns. The structure of many body proteins have been studied in this way. Sanger, in his research on the structure of insulin, took apart the insulin molecule by chemical means and determined the amino acids, making use of chromatography. Then he went on, in a series of beautiful experiments, to show how these amino acids are arranged in the insulin molecule as it is secreted by the cells of the pancreas.

Now that we know the structure of insulin, two very important things become possible. First, we can make a more intelligent study of the possible ways it works in the body. We can do this because we can figure out the way the insulin molecule interacts with some part of the cell wall to let sugar go through it faster. If we know how insulin works, we might be able to understand diabetes better, the disease which results when the pancreas stops secreting it. Second, we can devise ways to make insulin in the laboratory. It will then become much easier and cheaper to produce than the present expensive and laborious way it is extracted from the pancreas of cattle. Insulin is very expensive for diabetics who must take it every day; so by making it cheaper they will be greatly helped.

There is a disease of children that affects their minds. It is caused by a fault in the way the liver handles a particular amino acid called *phenylalanine*. Normally this amino acid is changed by the liver into another one called *tyrosine*. In this disease the conversion of phenylalanine to tyrosine is much slower than in normal children. Phenylalanine and some amino acids like it then pile up in the blood, and these somehow damage the brain. Using chromatography these abnormal amino acids were found in blood and urine; the cause of the disease was better understood, and now it can be easily recognized and treated. By reducing the amount of the phenylalanine in the young child's diet, its level in the blood can be kept down, and the mental retardation it causes can be prevented. So chromatography has made it much easier to recognize and follow the course of this condition, which no longer need cause the tragic mental defect if discovered early.

Just above each kidney is a yellowish pyramid-shaped organ called the adrenal gland. Each one of these is really two different glands in one; a center part secretes *adrenalin* — which affects the heart rate, blood pressure, and sugar level in the blood. The outer part, called the *cortex*, secretes several hormones that regulate carbohydrate and protein combustion as well as the rate of excretion of water and salt by the kidneys. It has been known that the manufacture and release of several of these cortex hormones is controlled by the pituitary gland at the base of the brain. But it was not known how this control was exerted or which of the cortex hormones was affected.

Chromatography has been used to answer several of these questions. The adrenal cortex–stimulating hormone (ACTH) of the pituitary gland can be prepared in fairly pure form. Experiments have been performed with animals so that blood coming from the adrenal gland can be collected. After several control blood samples are taken, ACTH is injected into the bloodstream, and at regular intervals afterwards more blood samples are drawn from the adrenal-gland vein. Now some of each of these blood samples is spotted on filter paper, and chromatograms are made of them to see what cortex hormones they contain. These chromatograms show that there is almost no hormone in the control samples, but after ACTH several new spots appear — each a different hormone. These become stronger with time, and later disappear. This shows that the hormone released from the adrenal cortex by ACTH lasts for a limited time, then stops. By comparing these chromatograms with similar ones of pure samples of cortex hormones, the different spots on the chromatograms from the blood samples can be identified.

In this way it was found that one of the hormones, called *hydrocortisone*, is the principal one released from the gland by ACTH stimulation. Smaller amounts of several others appeared as well. The study also showed that the hormone called *aldosterone* — which most powerfully affects water and salt excretion by the kidneys — is not regulated at all by pituitary ACTH.

Adrenal cortex hormones are given to people whose own adrenal glands have stopped making hormones because of disease. This treatment saves the lives of these people. Doctors want to give the hormones that the glands naturally secrete. So we can see how important the experiments with ACTH and adrenal vein blood chromatograms were. Never before did we know just what hormones the gland secretes naturally; now we can direct treatment much more intelligently on the basis of exact knowledge.

In the nucleus of each cell are the chromosomes which contain genes that determine how we are built and behave. The genes are passed on equally to both daughter cells when a cell divides. Genes are made of the magic substance that directs the complicated manufacture of new protein inside the cells during growth. This substance belongs to a class of chemicals called *nucleic acids*, and the one in the cell nucleus is known as *deoxyribonucleic acid*, or DNA for short. In recent years a series of brilliant discoveries have taught us a great deal about how DNA controls growth and the hereditary transmission of body characteristics, and in the process we have also learned much about how the large DNA molecule looks and is made. In these experiments chromatography played a big part.

The DNA molecule is made up of double strands of filament coiled about each other in a spiral. These are composed of a group of nitrogen containing substances called *purines* and *pyrimidines*. These are joined together end to end by phosphate molecules attached to sugars, and crosswise by bridges in which hydrogen atoms are bound to oxygen and nitrogen.

Biochemists have long suspected that if they could understand the arrangement of these purines and pyrimidines in the DNA of chromosomes, they could understand how the DNA determines the kinds of proteins that the cell makes and so how the body characteristics are determined. This research has involved the analysis of DNA structure, first by taking the molecules apart and analyzing their components, and second by preparing a test-tube system that makes DNA again in steps that can each be carefully followed. These two parts of the research brought the performers Nobel Prizes in medicine during recent years. Drs. Crick, Watson, and Wilkins received it in 1962 for determining the structure of DNA, and Dr. Arthur Kornberg was awarded it in 1959 for discovering the enzymes that make DNA.

In the step-by-step breakdown of DNA the purines and pyrimidines can be recognized by paper and ion-exchange chromatography. In this way not only was their identity made known but the ratios of their concentrations, and this became an important point in determining DNA structure. Since phosphate is an important part of the DNA molecule, much use was made of radioactive phosphorus in following the chemical reactions leading to completed DNA. At various stages in the procedure, the products were isolated and separated by chromatography. By seeing which ones contained the radioactive label, and at what time in the process, it was possible to identify the way the DNA was put together.

This whole story of the development and effects of chromatography in research could apply as well to a number of other methods we might have considered. But chromatography is so beautiful an example in its simplicity and usefulness in many situations in scientific research, that it seemed a good method to discuss.

XI   Who Does Research?

THE PEOPLE who do research come from many different backgrounds and work in a variety of institutions. Many go to a college or university and study biology or chemistry; some don't know at first that they are heading for research and may concentrate on literature or languages. However, this doesn't always hurt; in fact it might help them later to see problems more clearly and appreciate the relation between science and the other branches of learning. Sooner or later, though, the necessary science courses must be taken to prepare for the graduate work that will lead to a career in research.

This work may result in a doctor of philosophy degree (Ph.D.) in biology, chemistry, or physiology; or it may mean medical school, with an M.D. degree. In this case the decision to enter a career in research and teaching may come sometime during the four years of medical school, or afterward during the hospital internship. Some of these people go right into research without more formal training, usually learning how to do it from an older experienced person. Some decide to take more work toward the Ph.D. even though they already have the M.D. degree. Dr. Arthur Kornberg, who won the Nobel Prize in medicine in 1959, took a research fellowship after medical school and entered biochemical research and teaching without further graduate-school work. So there is no magic formula; each does it as his temperament and circumstances lead him. Nevertheless, today when the techniques are so specialized, the body of knowledge so big, and the trained mind so needed for good research, some form of advanced training beyond university undergraduate work is necessary for most.

The different ways we find ourselves in a particular field of work are interesting. In some people, and I am a good example, there is first the desire to do research, without a clear idea of the particular problem or even the broader field of interest. In this case you may meet a man whose research problems look interesting; so you join him, and after a time you find an interest you can call your own. This often leads to a period of special training and the development, with new techniques and new ideas, of a new field.

Some of us have a quite clear idea even before we enter research of what we want to do; some even have a specific problem in mind and a plan for attacking it. Usually, though, these people are only sure of the area in which they want to work, for example, the nervous system, heart, kidney, cancer, or rheumatic fever. Few beginning research students have a clearly thought-out idea for a problem and a definite plan of experiments for studying it, and that is all right. What we hope to see is a gradual change as the research training progresses to where the problem receives less and less direction from the teacher, and becomes more and more the student's own, with the teacher serving now as adviser rather than detailed guide. We like to see the person who is capable of independent thought and can do more and more of it as he goes on. Soon he stops needing so many ideas from his instructor and generates more of his own. As this happens he becomes an independent investigator.

Once trained, in one way or another, the time comes to find a position, and there are a number of different possibilities open at this point. Many men and women want to combine teaching and research; so they take jobs in a college or university. Some find these in an undergraduate department; others in a graduate school such as medical school. The life in this setting is very stimulating, because teaching and research, in the proper proportions, can benefit each other very much. Most people find they do a better job of teaching with minds kept active by research, and teaching can be a fine source of many good ideas for research. Since good research ideas often come from realizing a relation between things not previously seen as related, the preparation for teaching — particularly in an area outside one's narrower specialty interest — can often provide the opportunities for seeing these relations. I remember one such example where I had a new idea about kidney function while lecturing on the nervous control of breathing.

Others prefer to take full-time research jobs in an industrial laboratory, a government research institution like the National Institutes of Health outside Washing-

ton, or a private research institute like the Rockefeller Institute in New York City. Only a knowledge of yourself can tell you where you will fit best. Some have to try out one or the other for a while before knowing.

Generally, a position in a university, whether it is fulltime research or a mixture with teaching, provides the best freedom for work. The salary may not be as great as in industry, but the advantages of the university job make up for this difference in the minds of some. These differences are not so great today as a decade ago, because university salaries are better, and the good industries and government institutes have created research laboratories almost like a university's in terms of freedom of choice and development of a problem. They have found that the practical results of research are better under these circumstances.

Today there are two great forces competing for the trained research worker and teacher in biology and medicine. On the one hand, the universities are expanding rapidly to meet the educational needs of a growing population, so their needs for researchers and teachers are increasing. On the other hand, Congress and various special interest groups are putting on a lot of pressure to solve major health problems with more research. Because of this there is more and more money available to support the cost of the people, the institutes, and the very expensive equipment needed. Out of the success of the "crash program" to develop the atomic bomb during World War II has come the philosophy — not always good — that man's major health problems such as heart disease, polio, mental illness, diabetes, arthritis, and

RESEARCH is a $16 billion search for new facts and ideas
carried on by four groups of scientists.

| 70% Industry | 16% Federal Govt. | 10% Colleges and Universities | 4% Other Non-Profit Institutions |

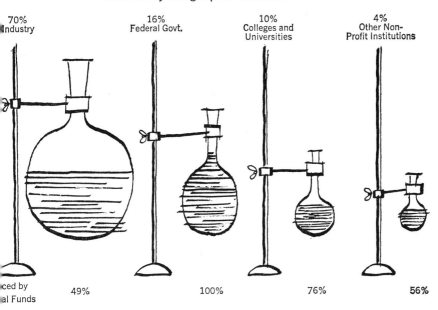

ced by
al Funds

49%   100%   76%   56%

cancer can be solved in a similar way by crash pro-
grams. All we need, they say, is lots of people at work
and lots of money to support them, and the answers will
surely come. Money and trained people are certainly
needed, but whether they will help the birth of the all-
important idea, we cannot say. Nevertheless, this public
philosophy has created many more full-time research
jobs, and this makes more chances for the people who
desire full-time research. It has also caused problems for
the universities who find it harder to fill their expanding
number of academic positions.

No matter how you enter it or where you find your
position, research has certain general features that make
it one of man's most demanding and most rewarding
creative activities.

XII Summing It Up

In these accounts of real discoveries I have tried to tell some of what science and research are all about. Science is nothing more than knowledge about nature, and research is the method science uses to create that knowledge. I hope I have succeeded in showing that the process of research involves much more than the mere observation and recording of facts. To be sure these are important in research, but the good scientist goes beyond this. He must be a clear and imaginative thinker. He must be able to have ideas in the form of good questions — often by seeing a new relation between things that had not been thought of as related before. Such ideas form the basis of the well-designed experiment which is the scientist's entry permit to nature's secret room.

During his experiment — designed from the scientist's intelligent guess at how nature might be — he records his observations and measurements. Then he frees himself as much as he can of his preconceived ideas, and asks: "What do these observations really mean? Do they confirm my original idea, or do they mean something different?" In asking the question this way the scientist reveals one of his finest qualities — his open-mindedness and first concern for the truth. He is only interested in discovering the truth to the best of his ability, and in the process of doing it he must always be willing to change his mind about the meaning of what he sees in nature, either on the basis of his own work, or that of others. Science demands this attitude and that experiments should be so designed and reported that others can repeat them with the same results, if they make them under the same controlled conditions as their originator did.

Scientists may, and do, differ about the interpretation of experimental observations. This is as it should be; this has been the history of science and how our views about nature have evolved. Many persons had *seen* fossils before Cuvier, Buffon, or Darwin, but none had seen the *meaning* in them that these men did for the first time. Sir Isaac Newton made accurate observations on the behavior of objects in motion, and deduced from these observations certain *laws* of motion which were accepted by the whole world, until Einstein came along. He saw a different meaning in the same observations, and by adding new ones, and making new calculations, came up with the idea that observations of bodies in motion can be different according to how one looks at them. The position of the observer can determine what he sees. So what he sees is *relative* to how he looks and measures; in this way Einstein's *relativity theory* was born.

Men back to earliest time had looked at the heart, lungs, blood vessels, and blood, and had put their own meaning in what they saw. They thought the blood

Harvey

pumped from the heart went to the liver where it was changed into animal spirits and dissipated. It wasn't until William Harvey questioned these assumptions in the seventeenth century and designed some ingenious experiments that he saw an entirely different meaning in the "facts" of anatomy and physiology before him. He saw that blood in the arteries flows away from the heart, while it flows toward the heart in the veins. He measured the amount of blood pumped out of the heart at each beat and calculated how much blood the body would have to contain if it all went to the liver without being used over again. From these and other experiments Harvey conceived — in his imagination — a set of ideas that formed the most logical explanation of the facts he had observed. Finally he concluded that the blood *circulates*, it goes round and round from heart to arteries to capillaries to veins, and back to the heart again, and is not lost in the process. This was a completely new idea in 1628 when Harvey published it.

How does an explanation of the facts, like this one, become a *law of nature?* The process takes place gradually in the minds of men and in the light of experience. No new explanation of the *facts* Harvey observed three hundred years ago has upset his interpretation, or offered us a better meaning for what he correctly saw. So by now Harvey's concept, or *theory*, of blood circulation has become a generally accepted *law*.

These considerations emphasize how different science and its methods are from the popularly held idea of them. It shows the scientist as a man with many of the same creative qualities as the artist, and using many of the same methods. Indeed the scientific research worker and the painter, writer, or composer are all experimentalists. The artists of the Renaissance *discovered* how to create an appearance of nearness or farness (called perspective) in a painting through employing the laws of color and geometry that had been discovered by scientists. They related as new ideas things that had been unrelated up till then, and as we have seen this is one of the finest characteristics of good research. So one can look on scientific research — in some of its aspects — as an art form.

How and when did modern science begin, and what has it meant for our understanding of life, the universe, and man's place in it? These are important questions that have interested many people because the findings of scientific research have deeply affected our society, how we live, the nature of war, the treatment of disease, and our traditional religious beliefs. So there isn't much that hasn't been affected by science.

It is very hard to say exactly when modern science was born; it's really as old as thinking man asking questions about himself and his surroundings. Certainly Aristotle's discovery of logic represented an important — though imperfect — contribution to modern scientific method. Pythagoras' discoveries in the fourth century B.C. of the harmonies of the tuned string, and the remarkable fact that in a right triangle the square of the hypotenuse equals the sum of the squares of the other two sides, represent first-class examples of really "modern" scientific discovery.

One could cite other examples of early revelations that are startling for their modernity. But I suppose the

Aristotle

really modern era of science started, dramatically, with Copernicus in 1543. His studies of the solar system did more to upset Western man's early religious beliefs than anything that had happened up to then.

The traditional Christian view in the Middle Ages regarded the earth as the center of the universe, and man as the highest, most special creation of God and His main concern. The stars of the heavens were supposed to be attached to a great revolving dome with a void out beyond. As we saw in the Darwin chapter, this view held that the earth and all its living creatures including man, had been created at one stroke by the almighty hand of God, and that man had survived in his present form through a series of catastrophes down through time.

Copernicus dared to question this view, and in his experiments he showed beyond doubt that the sun, rather than the earth, was the center of our system, and that the earth was just one of a group of planets revolving in their separate orbits around the sun. Thus the concept of the earth as the center of a closed universe was demolished, and now we know that our solar system is but a small part of a huge galaxy, and that the universe, without apparent limits, and expanding at a rapid rate, contains other galaxies with their solar systems throughout space. Many of these probably support some form of life — perhaps more intelligent than man.

Several other major discoveries of science have served to demolish the medieval view of man, and to create a serious conflict between the worlds of science and religion. The first of these was the one already con-

Copernicus

sidered, Darwin's theory of evolution. This, again, removed man from his lofty position as the special child of
God, and regarded him — along with the apes — as
only one stage in the evolution of living things. The ar-
guments over this doctrine are much less intense today,
but even now in the state of Tennessee it is forbidden to
teach the theory of evolution in public schools.

In 1865 Gregor Mendel, an Augustinian monk at
Brunn in Bohemia, announced his discovery of the law
of heredity following his experiments on garden peas.
Again these findings reduced the explanation of what
we are to a series of mechanisms carried out by our
genes according to unchangeable laws of nature. Of
course in the ordered workings of these beautiful mechanisms one can also see the hand of God, if he chooses.

Mendel

Einstein's publication of his theories of relativity still further shook the structure of beliefs about physics that had been accepted for nearly three hundred years; even though Newton had mainly seen a divine significance in his original laws, and had undertaken his studies in the first place for religious reasons.

The final devastating blow was dealt by Dr. Sigmund Freud in Vienna during the late nineteenth and early twentieth centuries, with his discovery of psychoanalysis and what it told him of the meaning of the subconscious mind. Here was man choosing certain types of behavior not because he was motivated by high purpose as a child of God but driven instead by a whole host of uncontrolled forces coming up out of his subconscious mind.

It is easy to see the very deep effect these and many

other revelations of science have had on our traditional thinking as they have appeared one after another. Today our whole society is shaped to a very large extent by the revolution in science which has made possible the products of technology, and therefore our high standard of living in the countries of Europe and North America.

The argument between science and religion is dying down, but now a new type of conflict about science has developed in the mind of the public. On the one hand, the miraculous discoveries in medicine and public health have made possible longer life freer of disease. Man can now turn his energies toward his finest creative work. On the other hand, however, the discoveries of science have produced the atomic and hydrogen bombs that now make it possible for mankind to erase himself — and all other forms of life — from the face of the earth. For these reasons many people regard science as both the savior and the destroyer of mankind. We can at the same time discover insulin or penicillin to save millions of lives and atomic warheads that can kill all a country's people ten times over.

So the scientist is regarded with suspicion because of his devilish inventions. Yet we cannot and do not want to do without him because we are not prepared to abolish the untold benefits he has brought to mankind. What to do, then? What is an acceptable, creative, workable view of science and the scientist?

First, I hope more people can understand science for what it is, and the main purpose of this book is to help do just that. To know about a thing removes some of the myth that surrounds it while it is misunderstood. I hope

I have portrayed the story of the scientist at his work, and science as one of man's noblest pursuits, along with the arts and religion. J. R. Bronowski has pointed out that science is the one pursuit of man that is dedicated — by general consent — to the truth. The scientist must put aside his own ambitions for personal gain or profit, and serve the purposes of truth. So science rests on an ethic of the purest kind. What a world this would be if this same aim were shared by businessmen, politicians, and nations in their relations with one another!

Secondly, we need to separate the thing called *science* and the persons who are scientists from the uses society and governments make of the discoveries of science. Should physicists stop working on atomic physics because governments — with the help of the physicists — can make atomic bombs? Should bacteriologists refrain from studying microbial disease because those diseases can be mass-produced in a population by the techniques of bacteriological warfare? I think not. Lord Rutherford's magnificent discovery of atomic structure made possible not only the knowledge that led to atomic and hydrogen bombs, but also to the healing use of radioactive iodine in the treatment of overactivity in the thyroid gland.

No, I believe that our salvation will come not because we abolish science and its practitioners, but because we expand and renew education, experience a broader public belief in the dignity of man and the formation of a private and public policy that expresses it at all levels of action. This means the greater humanization of science in our society at local, national, and international levels.

It means that the uses of science in the expression of national policy must be determined according to the picture of man and his finest purpose as revealed to us in literature, art, philosophy, the religions, and the lives of individuals dedicated to creative purpose. It is at this level that the culture of science becomes merged with the general body of tradition.

Additional Reading

BRONOWSKI, JACOB. *Science and Human Values*. New York: Messner, 1956.

BUTTERFIELD, HERBERT. *The Origins of Modern Science*. New York: Macmillan, 1951.

DARWIN, CHARLES R. *The Origin of Species*. New York: Modern Library, 1936.

EISELEY, LOREN. *Darwin's Century*. Garden City, New York: Doubleday, 1958.

——. *The Firmament of Time*. New York: Atheneum, 1960.

HARRIS, SEALE. *Banting's Miracle, the Story of the Discoverer of Insulin*. Philadelphia: Lippincott, 1946.

HINGSTON, R. W. G. *Darwin*. London: Duckworth, 1934.

HOGBEN, LANCELOT. *Science for the Citizen*. New York: Knopf, 1938.

LOEWI, OTTO. "An Autobiographic Sketch," *Perspectives in Biology and Medicine*, IV (1960-1961), 3-26.

MAUROIS, ANDRÉ. *The Life of Sir Alexander Fleming, Discoverer of Penicillin*. Translated from the

French by Gerard Hopkins. New York: Dutton, 1959.

SINGER, CHARLES J. *A Short History of Scientific Ideas to 1900.* Oxford: Clarendon Press, 1959.

Index